OUR EARTH

OUR EARTH

GLOBAL WARMING
THE EVIDENCE

KONECKY&KONECKY

Konecky & Konecky
72 Ayers Point Rd.
Old Saybrook, CT 06475

10 digit ISBN: 1-56852-638-5
13 digit ISBN: 978-1-56852-638-6

All images: AP Images

Selections of The Stern Review are reproduced under license from HM Treasury 1 Horse Guards Road London SW1A 2HQ, United Kingdom

Printed in China

INTRODUCTION

I t wasn't that long ago that we were reading about global warming and how it may become a major problem in 50 years. Have you noticed what has been happening over the past few years? Are we ready for what is about to happen in the next 50 years? The simple answer is no. Governments continue to *discuss* what could be done and we continue to exist in the only way we know how - by using energy that has for the past 50 years, steadily caused our current environment to disintegrate.

I happen to live in the driest city, the driest State and the driest continent in the world where I have personally observed a steady rise in summer temperatures, a decline in rainfall and warmer winters. There is simply no rain and this means that everything suffers.

While billions are being spent by western governments on useless wars and space exploration, our very existence is being ignored.

An increase in global temperatures can in turn cause other changes, including a rising sea level and changes in the amount and pattern of precipitation. These changes may increase the frequency and intensity of extreme weather events, such as floods, droughts, heat waves, hurricanes, and tornados. Other consequences include higher or lower agricultural yields, glacier retreat, reduced summer streamflows, species extinctions and increases in the ranges of disease vectors. Warming is expected to affect the number and magnitude of these events.

Our Earth brings to you the evidence that we have all largely ignored. Please take the time to read sections of the Stern review included in this book. This valuable study was commissioned by the Government of the United Kingdom. Sir Nick Stern lead a major review on the economics of climate change to understand more comprehensively the nature of the economic challenges and how they can be met, in the UK and globally.

With the hottest years on recent record and the promise of more to come, I urge you to help our planet in your own way. There are many small things we can all do to raise awareness and to make the world a great place to live for our children and grandchildren.

Here is my small contribution.

Peter Murray
Australia
2007

How Climate Change Will Affect People Around The World

Climate change threatens the basic elements of life for people around the world – access to water, food, health, and use of land and the environment. On current trends, average global temperatures could rise by 2 - 3°C within the next fifty years or so, leading to many severe impacts, often mediated by water, including more frequent droughts and floods.

• Melting glaciers will increase flood risk during the wet season and strongly reduce dry-season water supplies to one-sixth of the world's population, predominantly in the Indian sub-continent, parts of China, and the Andes in South America.

• Declining crop yields, especially in Africa, are likely to leave hundreds of millions without the ability to produce or purchase sufficient food - particularly if the carbon fertilisation effect is weaker than previously thought, as some recent studies suggest. At mid to high latitudes, crop yields may increase for moderate temperature rises (2 – 3°C), but then decline with greater amounts of warming.

• Ocean acidification, a direct result of rising carbon dioxide levels, will have major effects on marine ecosystems, with possible adverse consequences on fish stocks.

• Rising sea levels will result in tens to hundreds of millions more people flooded each year with a warming of 3 or 4°C. There will be serious risks and increasing pressures for coastal protection in South East Asia (Bangladesh and Vietnam), small islands in the Caribbean and the Pacific, and large coastal cities, such as Tokyo, Shanghai, Hong Kong, Mumbai, Calcutta, Karachi, Buenos Aires, St Petersburg, New York, Miami and London.

• Climate change will increase worldwide deaths from malnutrition and heat stress. Vector-borne diseases such as malaria and dengue fever could become more widespread if effective control measures are not in place. In higher latitudes, cold-related deaths will decrease.

• By the middle of the century, 200 million more people may become permanently displaced due to rising sea levels, heavier floods, and more intense droughts, according to one estimate.

• Ecosystems will be particularly vulnerable to climate change, with one study estimating that around 15 – 40% of species face extinction with 2°C of warming. Strong drying over the Amazon, as predicted by some climate models, would result in dieback of the forest with the highest biodiversity on the planet.

The consequences of climate change will become disproportionately more damaging with increased warming. Higher temperatures will increase the chance of triggering abrupt and large-scale changes that lead to regional disruption, migration and conflict.

• Warming may induce sudden shifts in regional weather patterns like the monsoons or the El Niño. Such changes would have severe consequences for water availability and flooding in tropical regions and threaten the livelihoods of billions.

• Melting or collapse of ice sheets would raise sea levels and eventually threaten at least 4 million Km2 of land, which today is home to 5% of the world's population.

2006 Was Earth's Fifth Warmest Year

Leslie McCarthy   Goddard Institute for Space Studies

THE HOTTEST YEARS ON RECORD

RANK	YEAR
1	2005
2	1998
3	2002
4	2003
5	2006
6	2004
7	2001
8	1997
9	1990
10	1995
11	1999
12	2000
13	1991
14	1987
15	1988
16	1994
17	1983
18	1996
19	1944
20	1989

Climatologists at the NASA Goddard Institute for Space Studies (GISS) in New York City have found that 2006 was the fifth warmest year in the past century.

Other groups that study climate change also rank these years as among the warmest, though the exact rankings vary depending upon details of the analyses. Results differ especially in regions of sparse measurements, where scientists use alternative methods of estimating temperature change.

Goddard Institute researchers used temperature data from weather stations on land, satellite measurements of sea surface temperature since 1982 and data from ships for earlier years.

"2007 is likely to be warmer than 2006," said James Hansen, director of NASA GISS, "and it may turn out to be the warmest year in the period of instrumental measurements. Increased warmth is likely this year because an El Nino is underway in the tropical Pacific Ocean and because of continuing increases in human-made greenhouse gases."

Most places on the globe have warmed in recent decades, with the greatest warming at high latitudes in the Arctic Ocean, Alaska, Siberia and the Antarctic Peninsula. Most ocean areas have warmed. Climatologists say that warming is not due to local effects of heat pollution in urban areas, a point demonstrated by warming in remote areas far from major cities.

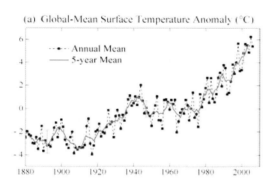

(a) Global-Mean Surface Temperature Anomaly (°C)

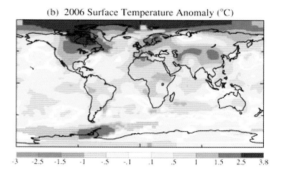

(b) 2006 Surface Temperature Anomaly (°C)

Images above: The upper graph shows global annual surface temperatures relative to 1951 to 1980 mean, based on surface air measurements at meteorological stations and ship and satellite measurements for sea surface temperature. Over the past 30 years the Earth has warmed by about 0.6°C or 1.08°F. The lower image is a color map of temperature anomalies in 2006 relative to the 1951 to 1980 mean. Areas that were warmest in 2006 are in red, and areas that have cooled are in blue. Note that the Arctic has warmed significantly. These temperatures are for the calendar year 2006.

This image shows a basic demonstration of the increase in annual mean temperature in five year increments from 1880 through 2006. Warmest temperatures are in red.

Global Warming - **FACTS**

Global average near-surface atmospheric temperature rose 0.6 ± 0.2 °Celsius (1.1 ± 0.4 °Fahrenheit) in the 20th century. The prevailing scientific opinion on climate change is that "most of the warming observed over the last 50 years is attributable to human activities." The main cause of the human-induced component of warming is the increased atmospheric concentration of greenhouse gases (GHGs) such as carbon dioxide (CO_2), which leads to warming of the surface and lower atmosphere by increasing the greenhouse effect. Greenhouse gases are released by activities such as the burning of fossil fuels, land clearing, and agriculture.

Models referenced by the Intergovernmental Panel on Climate Change (IPCC) predict that global temperatures may increase by 1.4 to 5.8 °C (2.5 to 10.5 °F) between 1990 and 2100. The uncertainty in this range results from both the difficulty of predicting the volume of future greenhouse gas emissions and uncertainty about climate sensitivity.

An increase in global temperatures can in turn cause other changes, including a rising sea level and changes in the amount and pattern of precipitation. These changes may increase the frequency and intensity of extreme weather events, such as floods, droughts, heat waves, hurricanes, and tornados. Other consequences include higher or lower agricultural yields, glacier retreat, reduced summer streamflows, species extinctions and increases in the ranges of disease vectors. Warming is expected to affect the number and magnitude of these events; however, it is difficult to connect particular events to global warming. Although most studies focus on the period up to 2100, warming (and sea level rise) is expected to continue past then, since CO_2 has a long average atmospheric lifetime.

Remaining scientific uncertainties include the exact degree of climate change expected in the future, and especially how changes will vary from region to region across the globe. A hotly contested political and public debate has yet to be resolved, regarding whether anything should be done, and what could be cost-effectively done to reduce or reverse future warming, or to deal with the expected consequences. Most national governments have signed and ratified the Kyoto Protocol aimed at combating global warming.

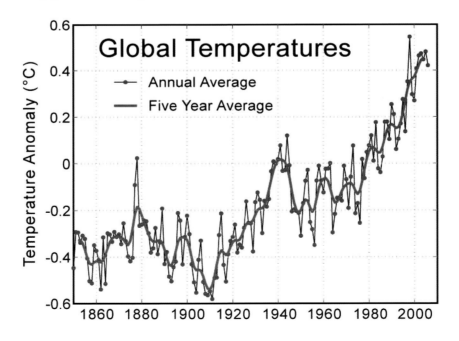

Visitors view the ice cave in Boulder Glacier at Glacier National Park, in July 1932. The same area is shown in this 1988 photo. If the glaciers at Glacier National Park continue melting at their current rate, they will be gone by 2050.

Global Warming - **FACTS**
Historical Warming of The Earth

Relative to the period 1860–1900, global temperatures on both land and sea have increased by 0.75 °C (1.4 °F), according to the instrumental temperature record. Since 1979, land temperatures have increased about twice as fast as ocean temperatures (0.25 °C/decade against 0.13 °C/decade (Smith, 2005). Temperatures in the lower troposphere have increased between 0.12 and 0.22 °C per decade since 1979, according to satellite temperature measurements. Over the one or two thousand years before 1850, world temperature is believed to have been relatively stable, with possibly regional fluctuations such as the Medieval Warm Period or the Little Ice Age.

Based on estimates by NASA's Goddard Institute for Space Studies, 2005 was the warmest year since reliable, widespread instrumental measurements became available in the late 1800s, exceeding the previous record set in 1998 by a few hundredths of a degree. Estimates prepared by the World Meteorological Organisation and the UK Climatic Research Unit concluded that 2005 was still only the second warmest year, behind 1998.

Depending on the time frame, a number of temperature records are available based on different data sets. The longest perspective is available from various proxy records for recent millennia; see temperature record of the past 1000 years for a discussion of these records and their differences. An approximately global instrumental record of temperature near the earth's surface begins in about 1860. Global observations of the atmosphere well above the earth's surface using data from radiosondes began shortly after World War II. Satellite temperature measurements of the tropospheric temperature date from 1979. The attribution of recent climate change is clearest for the most recent period of the last 50 years, for which the most detailed data are available.

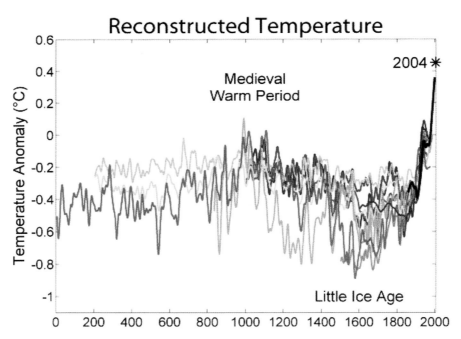

Two millennia of mean surface temperatures according to different reconstructions, each smoothed on a decadal scale. The unsmoothed, annual value for 2004 is also plotted for reference.

Genoa

An Italian police car, at bottom, patrols the snow-covered streets in Genoa's harbour, northwestern Italy, Thursday, March 3, 2005. A cold spell from Siberia hit the Italian peninsula characterised by unusually chilly temperatures for March in all cities.

Global Warming - **FACTS**
Causes

The climate system varies both through natural, "internal" processes as well as in response to variations in external "forcing" from both human and non-human causes, including solar activity, volcanic emissions, and greenhouse gases. Climatologists agree that the earth has warmed recently. The detailed causes of this change remain an active field of research, but the scientific consensus identifies greenhouse gases as the primary cause of the recent warming. Outside of the scientific community, however, this conclusion can be controversial.

Adding carbon dioxide (CO_2) or methane (CH_4) to Earth's atmosphere, with no other changes, will make the planet's surface warmer; greenhouse gases create a natural greenhouse effect without which temperatures on Earth would be an estimated 30 °C (54 °F) lower, and the Earth uninhabitable. It is therefore not correct to say that there is a debate between those who "believe in" and "oppose" the theory that adding carbon dioxide or methane to the Earth's atmosphere will, absent any mitigating actions or effects, result in warmer surface temperatures on Earth. Rather, the debate is about what the net effect of the addition of carbon dioxide and methane will be, when allowing for compounding or mitigating factors.

One example of an important feedback process is ice-albedo feedback. The increased CO_2 in the atmosphere warms the Earth's surface and leads to melting of ice near the poles. As the ice melts, land or open water takes its place. Both land and open water are on average less reflective than ice, and thus absorb more solar radiation. This causes more warming, which in turn causes more melting, and the cycle continues.

Due to the thermal inertia of the earth's oceans and slow responses of other indirect effects, the Earth's current climate is not in equilibrium with the forcing imposed by increased greenhouse gases. Climate commitment studies indicate that, even if greenhouse gases were stabilised at present day levels, a further warming of perhaps 0.5 °C to 1.0 °C (0.9–1.8 °F) would still occur.

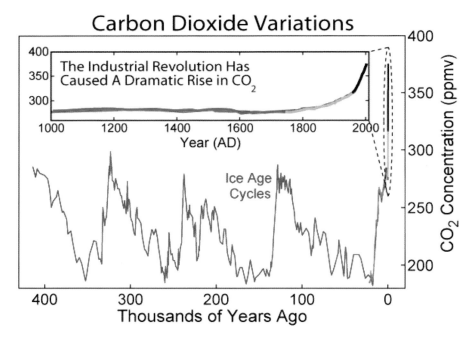

Carbon dioxide during the last 400,000 years and the rapid rise since the Industrial Revolution; changes in the Earth's orbit around the Sun, known as Milankovitch cycles, are believed to be the pacemaker of the 100,000 year ice age cycle.

Jerusalem

A Jerusalem resident walks with an umbrella under snow-covered palm trees next to Damascus Gate at Jerusalem's Old City Wednesday March 18, 1998. Several inches of snow blanketed Jerusalem and Northern Israel shutting down schools and paralysing public transportation.

This satellite image released by NASA Wednesday Sept. 28, 2005 shows the minimum concentration of Arctic sea ice in 1979. New satellite observations show that sea ice in the Arctic is melting faster while air temperatures in the region are rising sharply, scientists say. Since 2002, satellite data have revealed unusually early springtime melting in areas north of Siberia and Alaska. Now the melting trend has spread throughout the Arctic, according to a national collaboration of scientists study released by the University of Colorado at Boulder's National Snow and Ice Data Centre statement released Wednesday Sept. 28, 2005.

Arctic Sea

Global Warming - FACTS
Greenhouse Gases in the Atmosphere

Greenhouse gases are transparent to shortwave radiation from the sun, the main source of heat on the Earth. However, they absorb some of the longer infrared radiation emitted by the Earth, thereby reducing radiational cooling and hence raising the temperature of the Earth. How much they warm the world by is shown in their global warming potential. The measure of the response to increased GHGs, and other anthropogenic and natural climate forcings is climate sensitivity. It is found by observational and model studies. This sensitivity is usually expressed in terms of the temperature response expected from a doubling of CO2 in the atmosphere. The current literature estimates sensitivity in the range 1.5-4.5 °C (2.7-8.1 °F).

The atmospheric concentrations of carbon dioxide and methane have increased by 31% and 149% respectively above pre-industrial levels since 1750. This is considerably higher than at any time during the last 650,000 years, the period for which reliable data has been extracted from ice cores. From less direct geological evidence it is believed that carbon dioxide values this high were last attained 40 million years ago. About three-quarters of the anthropogenic (man-made) emissions of carbon dioxide to the atmosphere during the past 20 years are due to fossil fuel burning. The rest of the anthropogenic emissions are predominantly due to land-use change, especially deforestation.

The longest continuous instrumental measurement of carbon dioxide mixing ratios began in 1958 at Mauna Loa. Since then, the annually averaged value has increased monotonically by approximately 21% from the initial reading of 315 ppmv, as shown by the Keeling curve, to over 380 ppmv in 2006. The monthly CO2 measurements display small seasonal oscillations in an overall yearly uptrend; each year's maximum is reached during the northern hemisphere's late spring and declines during the northern hemisphere growing season as plants remove some CO2 from the atmosphere.

Methane, the primary constituent of natural gas, enters the atmosphere both from biological production and leaks from natural gas pipelines and other infrastructure. Some biological sources are natural, such as termites or forests, but others have been increased or created by agricultural activities such as the cultivation of rice paddies. Recent evidence indicates that methane concentrations have begun to stabilise, perhaps due to reductions in leakage from fuel transmission and storage facilities.

Future carbon dioxide levels are expected to continue rising due to ongoing fossil fuel usage. The rate of rise will depend on uncertain economic, sociological, technological, and natural developments. The IPCC Special Report on Emissions Scenarios gives a wide range of future carbon dioxide scenarios, ranging from 541 to 970 parts per million by the year 2100. Fossil fuel reserves are sufficient to reach this level and continue emissions past 2100, if coal and tar sands are extensively used.

Carbon sink ecosystems (forests and oceans are being degraded by pollutants. Degradation of major carbon sinks results in higher atmospheric carbon dioxide levels.

Globally, the majority of anthropogenic greenhouse gas emissions arise from fuel combustion. The remainder is accounted for largely by "fugitive fuel" (fuel consumed in the production and transport of fuel), emissions from industrial processes (excluding fuel combustion), and agriculture: these contributed 5.8%, 5.2% and 3.3% respectively in 1990. Current figures are broadly comparable. Around 17% of emissions are accounted for by the combustion of fuel for the generation of electricity. A small percentage of emissions come from natural and anthropogenic biological sources, with approximately 6.3% derived from agriculturally produced methane and nitrous oxide.

Positive feedback effects, such as the expected release of methane from the melting of permafrost peat bogs in Siberia (possibly up to 70,000 million tonnes), may lead to significant additional sources of greenhouse gas emissions. Note that the anthropogenic emissions of other pollutants—notably sulfate aerosols—exert a cooling effect; this partially accounts for the plateau/cooling seen in the temperature record in the middle of the twentieth century, though this may also be due to intervening natural cycles.

A view of the Ponte Vecchio (Old Bridge) during a snowfall in Florence, central Italy, Thursday, March 3, 2005. A cold spell from Siberia hit the Italian peninsula resulting in unusually cold temperatures for March.

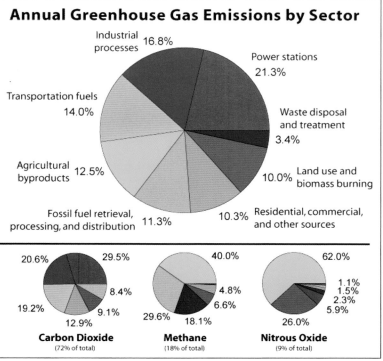

Annual Greenhouse Gas Emissions by Sector

Industrial processes 16.8%

Power stations 21.3%

Transportation fuels 14.0%

Waste disposal and treatment 3.4%

Agricultural byproducts 12.5%

Land use and biomass burning 10.0%

Fossil fuel retrieval, processing, and distribution 11.3%

Residential, commercial, and other sources 10.3%

20.6%   29.5%

8.4%

19.2%   9.1%

12.9%

Carbon Dioxide
(72% of total)

40.0%

4.8%

6.6%

29.6%   18.1%

Methane
(18% of total)

62.0%

1.1%
1.5%
2.3%
5.9%

26.0%

Nitrous Oxide
(9% of total)

Global Warming - **FACTS**
Ozone Depletion

The term ozone depletion is used to describe two distinct but related observations: a slow, steady decline of about 3 percent per decade in the total amount of ozone in Earth's stratosphere during the past twenty years; and a much larger, but seasonal, decrease in stratospheric ozone over Earth's polar regions during the same period. The latter phenomenon is commonly referred to as the ozone hole.

The detailed mechanism by which the polar ozone holes form is different from that for the mid-latitude thinning, but the most important process in both trends is believed to be catalytic destruction of ozone by atomic chlorine and bromine. The main source of these halogen atoms in the stratosphere is photodissociation of chlorofluorocarbon (CFC) compounds, commonly called freons, and of bromofluorocarbon compounds known as halons. These compounds are transported into the stratosphere after being emitted at the surface. Both ozone depletion mechanisms strengthened as emissions of CFCs and halons increased.

CFCs, halons and other contributory substances are commonly referred to as ozone-depleting substances (ODS). Since the ozone layer prevents most harmful UVB wavelengths (270–315 nm) of ultraviolet light (UV light) from passing through the Earth's atmosphere, observed and projected decreases in ozone have generated worldwide concern leading to adoption of the Montreal Protocol banning the production of CFCs and halons as well as related ozone depleting chemicals such as carbon tetrachloride and trichloroethane (also known as methyl chloroform). It is suspected that a variety of biological consequences such as increases in skin cancer, damage to plants, and reduction of plankton populations in the ocean's photic zone may result from the increased UV exposure due to ozone depletion.

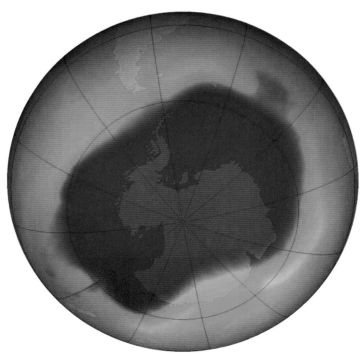

Image of the largest Antarctic ozone hole ever recorded in September 2006.

Paris

Heavy smog surrounds the Eiffel Tower in Paris Friday, July 15, 2005. A heatwave and high pollution levels swept though the city as Parisians left for summer holidays.

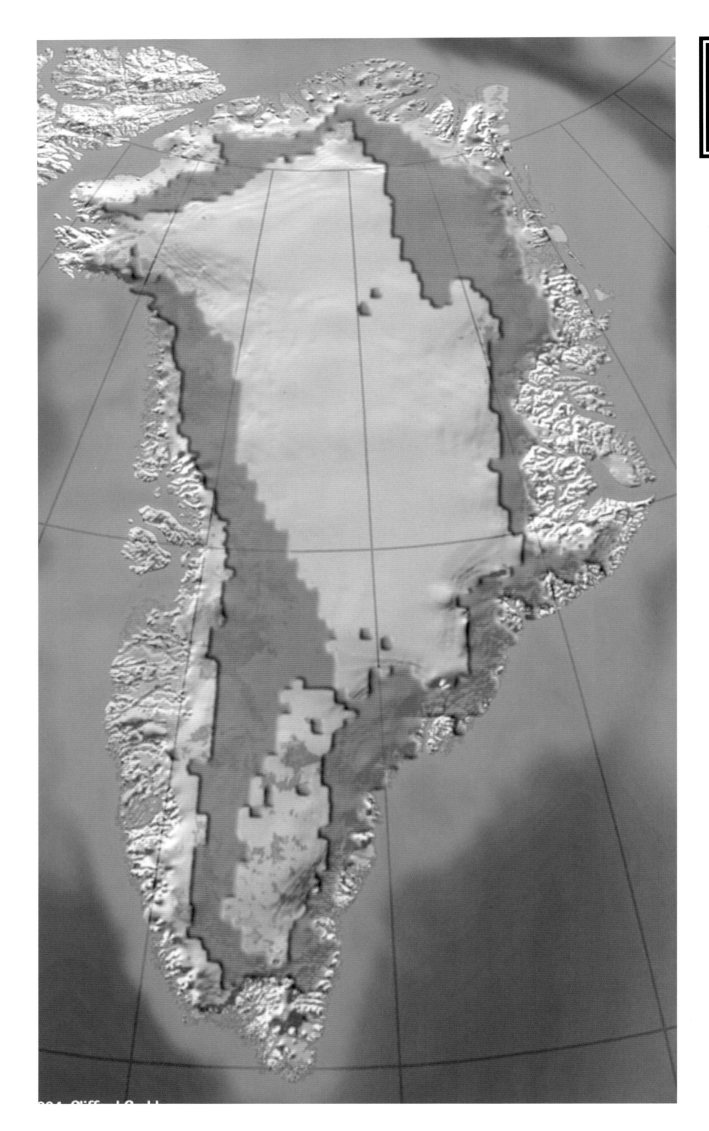

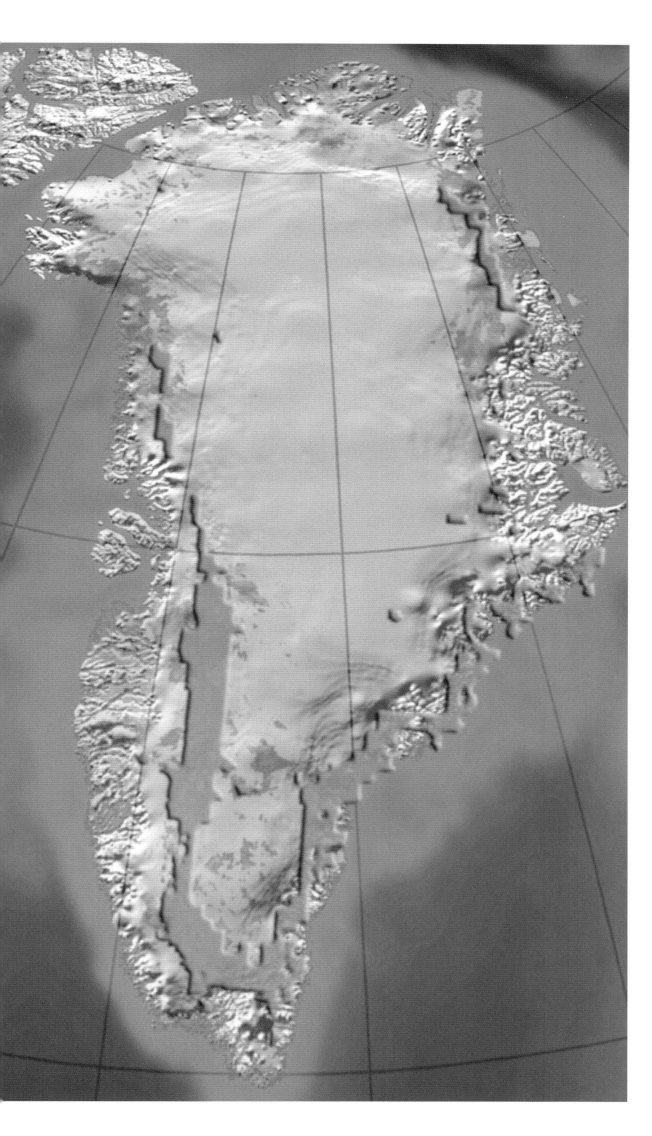

This graphic released by the Arctic Climate Impact Association indicates the seasonal melt extent of the Greenland Ice Sheet in 2002. The ice is melting and the heat is on for international delegates to find new ways to confront global warming.

Global Warming - **FACTS**
The Ozone Hole and its Causes

T he Antarctic ozone hole is an area of the Antarctic stratosphere in which the recent ozone levels have dropped to as low as 33% of their pre-1975 values. The ozone hole occurs during the Antarctic spring, from September to early December, as strong westerly winds start to circulate around the continent and create an atmospheric container. Within this "polar vortex", over 50% of the lower stratospheric ozone is destroyed during the antarctic spring.

As explained above, the overall cause of ozone depletion is the presence of chlorine-containing source gases (primarily CFCs and related halocarbons). In the presence of UV light, these gases dissociate, releasing chlorine atoms, which then go on to catalyse ozone destruction. The Cl-catalysed ozone depletion can take place in the gas phase, but it is dramatically enhanced in the presence of polar stratospheric clouds (PSCs).

These polar stratospheric clouds form during winter, in the extreme cold. Polar winters are dark, consisting of 3 months without solar radiation (sunlight). Not only lack of sunlight contributes to a decrease in temperature but also the "polar vortex" traps and chills air. Temperatures hover around or below -80 °C. These low temperatures form cloud particles and are composed of either nitric acid (Type I PSC) or ice (Type II PSC). Both types provide surfaces for chemical reactions that lead to ozone destruction.

The photochemical processes involved are complex but well understood. The key observation is that, ordinarily, most of the chlorine in the stratosphere resides in stable "reservoir" compounds, primarily hydrogen chloride (HCl) and chlorine nitrate ($ClONO_2$). During the Antarctic winter and spring, however, reactions on the surface of the polar stratospheric cloud particles convert these "reservoir" compounds into reactive free radicals (Cl and ClO). The clouds can also remove NO_2 from the atmosphere by converting it to nitric acid, which prevents the newly formed ClO from being converted back into $ClONO_2$.

The role of sunlight in ozone depletion is the reason why the Antarctic ozone depletion is greatest during spring. During winter, even though PSCs are at their most abundant, there is no light over the pole to drive the chemical reactions. During the spring, however, the sun comes out, providing energy to drive photochemical reactions, and melt the polar stratospheric clouds, releasing the trapped compounds.

Most of the ozone that is destroyed is in the lower stratosphere, in contrast to the much smaller ozone depletion through homogeneous gas phase reactions, which occurs primarily in the upper stratosphere.

Warming temperatures near the end of spring break up the vortex around mid-December. As warm, ozone-rich air flows in from lower latitudes, the PSCs are destroyed, the ozone depletion process shuts down, and the ozone hole heals.

Rome

A woman rides a bicycle with a sticker reading "Save Energy thank you" (Risparmia Energia grazie) in front of Rome's Colosseum, Sunday, March 6, 2005. People in Rome got around on public transportation, bicycles, on foot and even on horseback as car traffic was banned for several hours to lower air-pollution levels.

Greenland

A glacier off the Greenland ice cap is seen over western Greenland, Aug. 17, 2005. Scientists say the vast icy landscape is thinning, and many blame global warming. They worry about the implications for the life of Greenlanders, from the impact on fishing stocks to the ability of hunters' dogsleds to cross ice-covered fjords and inlets. NASA satellite monitoring shows Greenland glaciers dumping water into the sea at twice the rate of 1996. Such melting land ice is helping raise sea levels, along with the expansion of seawater as it warms.

China

Heavy clouds hang over Hangzhou, capital city of east China's Zhejiang Province, as Typhoon Haitang churned into southeastern China Tuesday, July 19, 2005, bringing torrential rain and high winds to coastal areas where more than 1 million people had fled their homes.

Greenland

An iceberg floats in the bay in Kulusuk, Greenland near the arctic circle Tuesday Aug 16, 2005. Unchecked global warming will devastate the world economy on the scale of the world wars and the Great Depression, a British government report said Monday Oct 30 2006, as the country launched a bid to convince doubters that environmentalism and economic growth can coincide

These photos released by the Glacier National Park Archives of the Shepard Glacier seen from Pyramid Peak in Glacier National Park - first in 1913, top, and then in 2005, reveal the dramatic change as the glacier has all but dissapeared. gradual warming continues to nibble away at the park's famed glaciers. Once as many as 150, they barely number 35 in June 2006.

These photos show the dramatic recession of the Grinnell Glacier as seen from the Grinnell Glacier Overlook off the Highline Trail in Glacier National Park. The first view taken in circa 1940 shows the early formation of Upper Grinnell Lake, a proglacier lake visible at the terminus of the glacier. The 2004 photo shows a dramatic increase in the size of the lake as a result of melting ice.

Global Warming - **FACTS**

How Climate Change Will Affect People Around The World

Water

P eople will feel the impact of climate change most strongly through changes in the distribution of water around the world and its seasonal and annual variability.

Water is an essential resource for all life and a requirement for good health and sanitation. It is a critical input for almost all production and essential for sustainable growth and poverty reduction. The location of water around the world is a critical determinant of livelihoods. Globally, around 70% of all freshwater supply is used for irrigating crops and providing food. 22% is used for manufacturing and energy (cooling power stations and producing hydro-electric power), while only 8% is used directly by households and businesses for drinking, sanitation, and recreation.

Climate change will alter patterns of water availability by intensifying the water cycle. Droughts and floods will become more severe in many areas. There will be more rain at high latitudes, less rain in the dry subtropics, and uncertain but probably substantial changes in tropical areas. Hotter land surface temperatures induce more powerful evaporation and hence more intense rainfall, with increased risk of flash flooding.

Differences in water availability between regions will become increasingly pronounced. Areas that are already relatively dry, such as the Mediterranean basin and parts of Southern Africa and South America, are likely to experience further decreases in water availability, for example several (but not all) climate models predict up to 30% decrease in annual runoff in these regions for a 2°C global temperature rise and 40 – 50% for 4°C. In contrast, South Asia and parts of Northern Europe and Russia are likely to experience increases in water availability (runoff), for example a 10 – 20% increase for a 2°C temperature rise and slightly greater increases for 4°C, according to several climate models.

These changes in the annual volume of water each region receives mask another critical element of climate change – its impact on year-to-year and seasonal variability. An increase in annual river flows is not necessarily beneficial, particularly in highly seasonal climates, because: (1) there may not be sufficient storage to hold the extra water for use during the dry season, and (2) rivers may flood more frequently. In dry regions, where runoff one-year-in-ten can be less than 20% of the average annual amount, understanding the impacts of climate change on variability of water supplies is perhaps even more crucial.

One recent study from the Hadley Centre predicts that the proportion of land area experiencing severe droughts at any one time will increase from around 10% today to 40% for a warming of 3 to 4°C, and the proportion of land area experiencing extreme droughts will increase from 3% to 30%. In Southern Europe, serious droughts may occur every 10 years with a 3°C rise in global temperatures instead of every 100 years if today's climate persisted.

As the water cycle intensifies, billions of people will lose or gain water. Some risk becoming newly or further water stressed, while others see increases in water availability. Seasonal and annual variability in water supply will determine the consequences for people through floods or droughts.

Global Warming - **FACTS**

How Climate Change Will Affect People Around The World

Water

Around one-third of today's global population live in countries experiencing moderate to high water stress, and 1.1 billion people lack access to safe water. Water stress is a useful indicator of water availability but does not necessarily reflect access to safe water. Even without climate change, population growth by itself may result in several billion more people living in areas of more limited water availability.

The effects of rising temperatures against a background of a growing population are likely to cause changes in the water status of billions of people. According to one study, temperature rises of 2°C will result in 1 – 4 billion people experiencing growing water shortages, predominantly in Africa, the Middle East, Southern Europe, and parts of South and Central America. In these regions, water management is already crucial for their growth and development. Considerably more effort and expense will be required on top of existing practices to meet people's demand for water. At the same time, 1 – 5 billion people, mostly in South and East Asia, may receive more water. However, much of the extra water will come during the wet season and will only be useful for alleviating shortages in the dry season if

storage could be created (at a cost). The additional water could also give rise to more serious flooding during the wet season.

Melting glaciers and loss of mountain snow will increase flood risk during the wet season and threaten dry-season water supplies to one-sixth of the world's population (over one billion people today).

Climate change will have serious consequences for people who depend heavily on glacier meltwater to maintain supplies during the dry season, including large parts of the Indian sub-continent, over quarter of a billion people in China, and tens of millions in the Andes. Initially, water flows may increase in the spring as the glacier melts more rapidly. This may increase the risk of damaging glacial lake outburst floods, especially in the Himalayas, and also lead to shortages later in the year. In the long run dry- season water will disappear permanently once the glacier has completely melted. Parts of the developed world that rely on mountain snowmelt (Western USA, Canadian prairies, Western Europe) will also have their summer water supply affected, unless storage capacity is increased to capture the "early water".

In the Himalaya-Hindu Kush region, meltwater from glaciers feeds seven of Asia's largest rivers, including 70% of the summer flow in the Ganges, which provides water to around 500 million people. In China, 23% of the population (250 million people) lives in the western region that depends principally on glacier meltwater. Virtually all glaciers are showing substantial melting in China, where spring stream-flows have advanced by nearly one month since records began. In the tropical Andes in South America, the area covered by glaciers has been reduced by nearly one-quarter in the past 30 years. Some small glaciers are likely to disappear completely in the next decade given current trends. Many large cities such as La Paz, Lima and Quito and up to 40% of agriculture in Andean valleys rely on glacier meltwater supplies. Up to 50 million people in this region will be affected by loss of dry-season water.

Global Warming - FACTS
How Climate Change Will Affect People Around The World
Food

In tropical regions, even small amounts of warming will lead to declines in yield. In higher latitudes, crop yields may increase initially for moderate increases in temperature but then fall.

Higher temperatures will lead to substantial declines in cereal production around the world, particularly if the carbon fertilisation effect is smaller than previously thought, as some recent studies suggest.

Food production will be particularly sensitive to climate change, because crop yields depend in large part on prevailing climate conditions (temperature and rainfall patterns). Agriculture currently accounts for 24% of world output, employs 22% of the global population, and occupies 40% of the land area. 75% of the poorest people in the world (the one billion people who live on less than $1 a day) live in rural areas and rely on agriculture for their livelihood.

Low levels of warming in mid to high latitudes (US, Europe, Australia, Siberia and some parts of China) may improve the conditions for crop growth by extending the growing season and/or opening up new areas for agriculture. Further warming will have increasingly negative impacts – the classic "hill function" - as damaging temperature thresholds are reached more often and water shortages limit growth in regions such as Southern Europe and Western USA. High temperature episodes can reduce yields by up to half if they coincide with a critical phase in the crop cycle like flowering.

The impacts of climate change on agriculture depend crucially on the size of the "carbon fertilisation" effect. Carbon dioxide is a basic building block for plant growth. Rising concentrations in the atmosphere may enhance the initial benefits of warming and even offset reductions in yield due to heat and water stress. Work based on the original predictions for the carbon fertilisation effect suggests that yields of several cereals (wheat and rice in particular) will increase for 2 or 3°C of warming globally, according to some models, but then start to fall once temperatures reach 3 or 4°C.33 Maize shows greater declines in yield with rising temperatures because its different physiology makes it less responsive to the direct effects of rising carbon dioxide. Correspondingly, world cereal production only falls marginally (1 – 2%) for warming up to 4°C. But the latest analysis from crops grown in more realistic field conditions suggests that the effect is likely to be no more than half that typically included in crop models. When a weak carbon fertilisation effect is used, worldwide cereal production declines by 5% for a 2°C rise in temperature and 10% for a 4°C rise. By 4°C, entire regions may be too hot and dry to grow crops, including parts of Australia. Agricultural collapse across large areas of the world is possible at even higher temperatures (5 or 6°C) but clear empirical evidence is still limited.

While agriculture in higher-latitude developed countries is likely to benefit from moderate warming (2 – 3°C), even small amounts of climate change in tropical regions will lead to declines in yield. Here crops are already close to critical temperature thresholds36 and many countries have limited capacity to make economy-wide adjustments to farming patterns. The impacts will be strongest across Africa and Western Asia (including the Middle East), where yields of the

Global Warming - **FACTS**
How Climate Change Will Affect People Around The World
Food

predominant regional crops may fall by 25 – 35% (weak carbon fertilisation) or 15 – 20% (strong carbon fertilisation) once temperatures reach 3 or 4°C. Maize-based agriculture in tropical regions, such as parts of Africa and Central America, is likely to suffer substantial declines, because maize has a different physiology to most crops and is less responsive to the direct effects of rising carbon dioxide.

Many of the effects of climate change on agriculture will depend on the degree of adaptation, which itself will be determined by income levels, market structure, and farming type, such as rain-fed or irrigated. Studies that take a more optimistic view of adaptation and assume that a substantial amount of land at higher latitudes becomes suitable for production find more positive effects of climate change on yield. But the transition costs are often ignored and the movement of population required to make this form of adaptation a reality could be very disruptive. At the same time, many existing estimates do not include the impacts of short-term weather events, such as floods, droughts and heatwaves. These have only recently been incorporated into crop models, but are likely to have additional negative impacts on crop production. Expansion of agricultural land at the expense of natural vegetation may itself exert additional effects on local climates with tropical deforestation leading to rainfall reductions because of less moisture being returned to the atmosphere once trees are removed.

Global Warming - **FACTS**
The Kyoto Protocol

The Kyoto Protocol is an agreement made under the United Nations Framework Convention on Climate Change (UNFCCC). Countries that ratify this protocol commit to reduce their emissions of carbon dioxide and five other greenhouse gases, or engage in emissions trading if they maintain or increase emissions of these gases.

The Kyoto Protocol now covers more than 160 countries globally and over 55% of global greenhouse gas (GHG) emissions.

At its heart, Kyoto establishes the following principles:

• Kyoto is underwritten by governments and is governed by global legislation enacted under the UN's aegis

• Governments are separated into two general categories: developed countries, referred to as Annex 1 countries (who have accepted GHG emission reduction obligations and must submit an annual greenhouse gas inventory); and developing countries, referred to as Non-Annex 1 countries (who have no GHG emission reduction obligations but may participate in the Clean Development Mechanism).

• Any Annex 1 country that fails to meet its Kyoto target will be penalised by having to submit 1.3 emission allowances in a second commitment period for every ton of GHG emissions they exceed their cap in the first commitment period (i.e, 2008-2012).

• By 2008-2012, Annex 1 countries have to reduce their GHG emissions by an average of 5% below their 1990 levels (for many countries, such as the EU member states, this corresponds to some 15% below their expected GHG emissions in 2008). While the average emissions reduction is 5%, national targets range from 8% reductions for the European Union to a 10% emissions increase for Iceland. Reduction targets expire in 2013.

• Kyoto includes "flexible mechanisms" which allow Annex 1 economies to meet their GHG targets by purchasing GHG emission reductions from elsewhere. These can be bought either from financial exchanges (such as the new EU Emissions Trading Scheme) or from projects which reduce emissions in non-Annex 1 economies under the Clean Development Mechanism (CDM), or in other Annex-1 countries under the JI.

• Only CDM Executive Board-accredited Certified Emission Reductions (CER) can be bought and sold in this manner. Under the aegis of the UN, Kyoto established this Bonn-based Clean Development Mechanism Executive Board to assess and approve projects ("CDM Projects") in Non-Annex 1 economies prior to awarding CERs. (A similar scheme called "Joint Implementation" or "JI" applies in transitional economies mainly covering the former Soviet Union and Eastern Europe).

• What this means in practice is that Non-Annex 1 economies have no GHG emission restrictions, but when a GHG emission reduction project (a "GHG Project") is implemented in these countries, that GHG Project will receive Carbon Credit which can be sold to Annex 1 buyers.

The Kyoto linking mechanisms are in place for two main reasons:

the cost of complying with Kyoto is prohibitive for many Annex 1 countries (especially those countries, such as Japan or the Netherlands for example, with highly efficient, low GHG polluting industries, and high prevailing environmental standards). Kyoto therefore allows these countries to purchase Carbon Credits instead of reducing GHG emissions

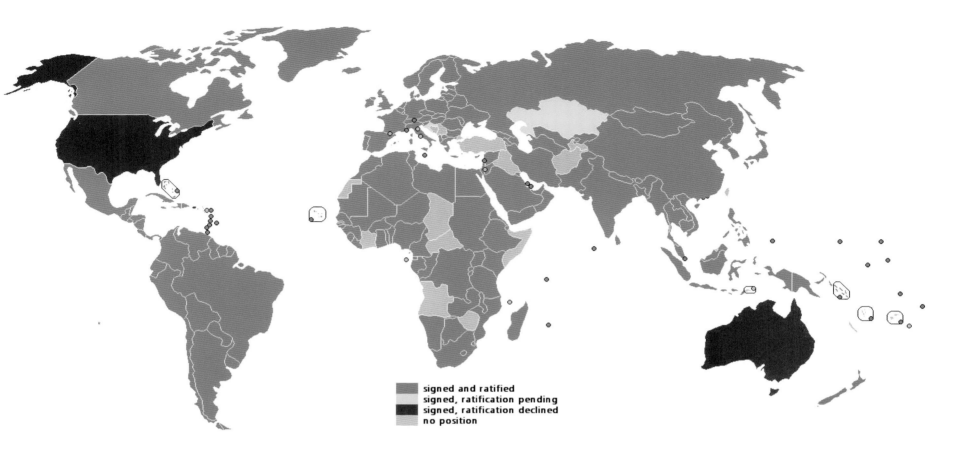

Participation in the Kyoto Protocol, where dark green indicates countries that have signed and ratified the treaty and yellow indicates states that have signed and hope to ratify the treaty. Australia and the United States have signed the treaty but refuse to ratify it.

domestically; and, this is seen as a means of encouraging Non-Annex 1 developing economies to reduce GHG emissions since doing so is now economically viable because of the sale of Carbon Credits.

All the Annex 1 economies have established Designated National Authorities to manage their GHG portfolios under Kyoto. Countries including Japan, Canada, Italy, the Netherlands, Germany, France, Spain and many more, are actively promoting government carbon funds and supporting multilateral carbon funds intent on purchasing Carbon Credits from Non-Annex 1 countries. These government organisations are working closely with their major utility, energy, oil & gas and chemicals conglomerates to try to acquire as many GHG Certificates as cheaply as possible.

Virtually all of the Non-Annex 1 countries have also set up their own Designated National Authorities to manage the Kyoto process (and specifically the "CDM process" whereby these host government entities decide which GHG Projects they do or do not wish to support for accreditation by the CDM Executive Board).

The objectives of these opposing groups are quite different. Annex 1 entities want Carbon Credits as cheaply as possible, whilst Non-Annex 1 entities want to maximise the value of Carbon Credits generated from their domestic GHG Projects.

Global Warming - **FACTS**
The Kyoto Protocol

T he treaty was negotiated in Kyoto, Japan in December 1997, opened for signature on March 16, 1998, and closed on March 15, 1999. The agreement came into force on February 16, 2005 following ratification by Russia on November 18, 2004. As of December 2006, a total of 169 countries and other governmental entities have ratified the agreement (representing over 61.6% of emissions from Annex I countries). Notable exceptions include the United States and Australia. Other countries, like India and China, which have ratified the protocol, are not required to reduce carbon emissions under the present agreement despite their relatively large populations.

According to article 25 of the protocol, it enters into force "on the ninetieth day after the date on which not less than 55 Parties to the Convention, incorporating Parties included in Annex I which accounted in total for at least 55% of the total carbon dioxide emissions for 1990 of the Parties included in Annex I, have deposited their instruments of ratification, acceptance, approval or accession." Of the two conditions, the "55 parties" clause was reached on May 23, 2002 when Iceland ratified. The ratification by Russia on 18 November 2004 satisfied the "55%" clause and brought the treaty into force, effective February 16, 2005.

According to a press release from the United Nations Environment Programme:

"The Kyoto Protocol is an agreement under which industrialised countries will reduce their collective emissions of greenhouse gases by 5.2% compared to the year 1990 (but note that, compared to the emissions levels that would be expected by 2010 without the Protocol, this target represents a 29% cut). The goal is to lower overall emissions of six greenhouse gases - carbon dioxide, methane, nitrous oxide, sulfur hexafluoride, HFCs, and PFCs - calculated as an average over the five-year period of 2008-12. National targets range from 8% reductions for the European Union and some others to 7% for the US, 6% for Japan, 0% for Russia, and permitted increases of 8% for Australia and 10% for Iceland."

It is an agreement negotiated as an amendment to the United Nations Framework Convention on Climate Change (UNFCCC, which was adopted at the Earth Summit in Rio de Janeiro in 1992). All parties to the UNFCCC can sign or ratify the Kyoto Protocol, while non-parties to the UNFCCC cannot. The Kyoto Protocol was adopted at the third session of the Conference of Parties (COP) to the UNFCCC in 1997 in Kyoto, Japan.

The United Nations Framework Convention on Climate Change agreed to a set of a "common but differentiated responsibilities." The parties agreed that;

• The largest share of historical and current global emissions of greenhouse gases has originated in developed countries;

• Per capita emissions in developing countries are still relatively low;

• The share of global emissions originating in developing countries will grow to meet their social and development needs.

In other words, China, India, and other developing countries were exempt from the requirements of the Kyoto Protocol because they were not the main contributors to the greenhouse gas emissions during the industrialisation period that is believed to be causing today's climate change.

However, critics of Kyoto argue that China, India, and other developing countries will soon be the top contributors to greenhouse gases. Also, without Kyoto restrictions on these countries, industries in developed countries will be driven towards these non-restricted countries, thus there is no net reduction in carbon.

The river bed of the Oued Tansift is shown in Marrakech after a three-year drought. Morocco, which embraces the ever-expanding Sahara desert, recently hosted a conference in the world's most ambitious effort to curtail the man-made greenhouse gases blamed for unnaturally heating Earth's atmosphere.

STERN REVIEW
The Economics of Climate Change

There is still time to avoid the worst impacts of climate change, if we take strong action now.

The scientific evidence is now overwhelming: climate change is a serious global threat, and it demands an urgent global response.

This Review has assessed a wide range of evidence on the impacts of climate change and on the economic costs, and has used a number of different techniques to assess costs and risks. From all of these perspectives, the evidence gathered by the Review leads to a simple conclusion: the benefits of strong and early action far outweigh the economic costs of not acting.

Climate change will affect the basic elements of life for people around the world – access to water, food production, health, and the environment. Hundreds of millions of people could suffer hunger, water shortages and coastal flooding as the world warms.

Using the results from formal economic models, the Review estimates that if we don't act, the overall costs and risks of climate change will be equivalent to losing at least 5% of global GDP each year, now and forever. If a wider range of risks and impacts is taken into account, the estimates of damage could rise to 20% of GDP or more.

In contrast, the costs of action – reducing greenhouse gas emissions to avoid the worst impacts of climate change – can be limited to around 1% of global GDP each year.

The investment that takes place in the next 10-20 years will have a profound effect on the climate in the second half of this century and in the next. Our actions now and over the coming decades could create risks of major disruption to economic and social activity, on a scale similar to those associated with the great wars and the economic depression of the first half of the 20th century. And it will be difficult or impossible to reverse these changes.

So prompt and strong action is clearly warranted. Because climate change is a global problem, the response to it must be international. It must be based on a shared vision of long-term goals and agreement on frameworks that will accelerate action over the next decade, and it must build on mutually reinforcing approaches at national, regional and international level.

Climate change could have very serious impacts on growth and development.

If no action is taken to reduce emissions, the concentration of greenhouse gases in the atmosphere could reach double its pre-industrial level as early as 2035, virtually committing us to a global average temperature rise of over 2°C. In the longer term, there would be more than a 50% chance that the temperature rise would exceed 5°C. This rise would be very dangerous indeed; it is equivalent to the change in average temperatures from the last ice age to today. Such a radical change in the physical geography of the world must lead to major changes in the human geography – where people live and how they live their lives.

Even at more moderate levels of warming, all the evidence – from detailed studies of regional and sectoral impacts of changing weather patterns through to economic models of the global effects – shows that climate change will have serious impacts on world output, on human life and on the environment.

All countries will be affected. The most vulnerable – the poorest countries and populations – will suffer earliest and most, even though they have contributed least to the causes of climate change. The costs of extreme weather, including floods, droughts and storms, are already rising, including for rich countries.

Adaptation to climate change – that is, taking steps to build resilience and minimise costs – is essential. It is no longer possible to prevent the climate change that will take place over the next two to three decades, but it is still possible to protect our societies and economies from its impacts to some extent – for example, by providing better information, improved planning and more climate-resilient crops and infrastructure. Adaptation will cost tens of billions of dollars a year in developing countries alone, and will put still further pressure on already scarce resources. Adaptation efforts, particularly in developing countries, should be accelerated.

The costs of stabilising the climate are significant but manageable; delay would be dangerous and much more costly.

The risks of the worst impacts of climate change can be substantially reduced if greenhouse gas levels in the atmosphere can be stabilised between 450 and 550ppm CO_2 equivalent (CO_2e). The current level is 430ppm CO_2e today, and it is rising at more than 2ppm each year. Stabilisation in this range would require emissions to be at least 25% below current levels by 2050, and perhaps much more.

Ultimately, stabilisation – at whatever level – requires that annual emissions be brought down to more than 80% below current levels.

This is a major challenge, but sustained long-term action can achieve it at costs that are low in comparison to the risks of inaction. Central estimates of the annual costs of achieving stabilisation between 500 and 550ppm CO_2e are around 1% of global GDP, if we start to take strong action now.

Costs could be even lower than that if there are major gains in efficiency, or if the strong co-benefits, for example from reduced air pollution, are measured. Costs will be higher if innovation in low-carbon technologies is slower than expected, or if policy-makers fail to make the most of economic instruments that allow emissions to be reduced whenever, wherever and however it is cheapest to do so.

It would already be very difficult and costly to aim to stabilise at 450ppm CO_2e. If we delay, the opportunity to stabilise at 500-550ppm CO_2e may slip away.

Action on climate change is required across all countries, and it need not cap the aspirations for growth of rich or poor countries.

The costs of taking action are not evenly distributed across sectors or around the world. Even if the rich world takes on responsibility for absolute cuts in emissions of 60-80% by 2050, developing countries must take significant action too. But developing countries should not be required to bear the full costs of this action alone, and they will not have to. Carbon markets in rich countries are already beginning to deliver flows of finance to support low-carbon development, including through the Clean Development Mechanism. A transformation of these flows is now required to support action on the scale required.

Action on climate change will also create significant business opportunities, as new markets are created in low-carbon energy technologies and other low-carbon goods and services. These markets could grow to be worth hundreds of billions of dollars each year, and employment in these sectors will expand accordingly.

The world does not need to choose between averting climate change and promoting growth and development. Changes in energy technologies and in the structure of economies have created opportunities to decouple growth from greenhouse gas emissions. Indeed, ignoring climate change will eventually damage economic growth.

Tackling climate change is the pro-growth strategy for the longer term, and it can be done in a way that does not cap the aspirations for growth of rich or poor countries.

A range of options exists to cut emissions; strong, deliberate policy action is required to motivate their take-up.

Emissions can be cut through increased energy efficiency, changes in demand, and through adoption of clean power, heat and transport technologies. The power sector around the world would need to be at least 60% decarbonised by 2050 for atmospheric concentrations to stabilise at or below 550ppm CO_2e, and deep emissions cuts will also be required in the transport sector.

Even with very strong expansion of the use of renewable energy and other low- carbon energy sources, fossil fuels could still make up over half of global energy supply in 2050. Coal will continue to be important in the energy mix around the world, including in fast-growing economies. Extensive carbon capture and storage will be necessary to allow the continued use of fossil fuels without damage to the atmosphere.

Cuts in non-energy emissions, such as those resulting from deforestation and from agricultural and industrial processes, are also essential.

With strong, deliberate policy choices, it is possible to reduce emissions in both developed and developing economies on the scale necessary for stabilisation in the required range while continuing to grow.

Climate change is the greatest market failure the world has ever seen, and it interacts with other market imperfections. Three elements of policy are required for an effective global response. The first is the pricing of carbon, implemented through tax, trading or regulation. The second is policy to support innovation and the deployment of low-carbon technologies. And the third is action to remove barriers to energy efficiency, and to inform, educate and persuade individuals about what they can do to respond to climate change.

Climate change demands an international response, based on a shared understanding of long-term goals and agreement on frameworks for action.

Many countries and regions are taking action already: the EU, California and China are among those with the most ambitious policies that will reduce greenhouse gas emissions. The UN Framework Convention on Climate Change and the Kyoto Protocol provide a basis for international co-operation, along with a range of partnerships and other approaches. But more ambitious action is now required around the world.

Countries facing diverse circumstances will use different approaches to make their contribution to tackling climate change. But action by individual countries is not enough. Each country, however large, is just a part of the problem. It is essential to create a shared international vision of long-term goals, and to build the international frameworks that will help each country to play its part in meeting these common goals.

Key elements of future international frameworks should include:

• Emissions trading: Expanding and linking the growing number of emissions trading schemes around the world is a powerful way to promote cost-effective reductions in emissions and to bring forward action in developing countries: strong targets in rich countries could drive flows amounting to tens of billions of dollars each year to support the transition to low-carbon development paths.

• Technology cooperation: Informal co-ordination as well as formal agreements can boost the effectiveness of investments in innovation around the world. Globally, support for energy R&D should at least double, and support for the deployment of new low-carbon technologies should increase up to five-fold. International co- operation on product standards is a powerful way to boost energy efficiency.

• Action to reduce deforestation: The loss of natural forests around the world contributes more to global emissions each year than the transport sector. Curbing deforestation is a highly cost-effective way to reduce emissions; large- scale international pilot programmes to explore the best ways to do this could get underway very quickly.

• Adaptation: The poorest countries are most vulnerable to climate change. It is essential that climate change be fully integrated into development policy, and that rich countries honour their pledges to increase support through overseas development assistance. International funding should also support improved regional information on climate change impacts, and research into new crop varieties that will be more resilient to drought and flood.

Climate Threat Advances "Doomsday Clock"

Experts assessing the dangers posed to civilisation have added climate change to the prospect of nuclear annihilation as the greatest threats to humankind. The "Doomsday Clock", established in 1947 by the "Bulletin of the Atomic Scientists" to warn the world of the dangers of nuclear weapons, was just moved from 7 to 5 minutes to midnight largely on the basis of climate change concerns. In addition to highlighting continued concerns with nuclear warfare (which in itself would dramatically alter the climate), and particularly proliferation as nuclear energy spreads, for the first time the clock moved because of "destruction of human habitats wreaked by climate change brought on by human activities... global warming poses a dire threat to human civilisation that is second only to nuclear weapons." Since its inception the clock has moved from as much as 17 minutes to 2 minutes to doomsday. The recent change is the first since 2002. Theoretical physicist Stephen Hawking said "we foresee great peril if governments and societies do not take action now to render nuclear weapons obsolete and to prevent further climate change." We at Ecological Internet concur; indeed, the warnings echo sentiments found in a recent Earth Meanders personal essay entitled "Earth Prophecy" by Dr. Glen Barry. No one can say with certainty how soon if ever the human race will annihilate itself. Yet with the basic science that humankind is causing global heating settled, and many of the projections made regarding impacts upon the Earth of over-population and environmental destruction coming true (in some cases many times more abruptly than expected), and with increasing militarisation including nuclear, clearly humanity has moved more closely to its own demise.www.climateark.org

Personal Sacrifice and the Climatic System

As the science of climate change becomes more widely known, we are entering a period of angst where the reality of climatic system collapse is accepted, yet the search for climate solutions lags. One dispute is to what extent individuals must sacrifice modern conveniences to reduce emissions; such as driving less, eating less meat and many other energy conserving activities; or whether the required necessary changes are of such a scale like public mass transit, global carbon caps and a carbon tax, which can only be carried out by governments. Given we must reduce emissions dramatically, by some 60% and perhaps more as soon as possible, the answer is both. We are very disappointed in Tony Blair's statement that we should all carry on with our air travel because science will find an answer to the problem. The hard reality is that some degree of personal sacrifice is going to be required. Additionally, emissions cannot get to their required levels without rich nations dramatically cutting their emissions and allowing poor nations to increase to equal levels. This approach is called contract and converge. President Bush selfishly says America will not set mandatory emissions caps because developing countries refuse to do so immediately, when our emissions are up to 30 times that of poor nations. Climate solutions require that emissions must be reduced equitably, both personally and by governments. We should work hard to reduce our own carbon footprint while joining the people's movement to bring about societal change sufficient to achieve long-term, equitable and just global ecological sustainability. www.climateark.org

Kyoto Protocol Australia

Despite the fact that Australia was at the time of the negotiation already one of the biggest emitters on a per capita basis (albeit the lowest on a per square kilometre basis due to low overall population density), the country was granted a target of 8% increase. This is because Australia used its relative smallness as a negotiation tool while other big players were negotiating. The result of the negotiation was reported in the Australian media as being to Australia's advantage. Nonetheless, the Australian Prime Minister, John Howard, has refused to ratify the Agreement and has argued that the protocol would cost Australians jobs, due to countries with booming economies and massive populations such as China and India not having any reduction obligations. By way of example, if Australia were to shut down all of its coal fired power stations, within 12 months China would have produced so much extra pollution because of its industrial growth that it would have negated the shutting down of those Australian power stations. Further, the Government takes the view that Australia is already doing enough to cut emissions; the Australian government has recently pledged $300 million over the next three years to reduce Greenhouse gas emissions. The Federal Opposition, the Australian Labor Party, is in full support of the protocol and it is currently a heavily debated issue within the political establishment. The opposition claims ratifying the protocol is a "risk free" prospect as they claim Australia would already be meeting the obligations the protocol would impose. As of 2005, Australia was the world's largest emitter per capita of greenhouse gases. The Australian government, along with the United States, agreed to sign the Asia Pacific Partnership on Clean Development and Climate at the ASEAN regional forum on 28 July 2005.

Age of King Coal Must End, R.I.P.

There is no, and can never be, such a thing as "Clean Coal." Widespread burying of CO2 which is the basis for "Clean Coal" claims is an industry PR lie that is decades away, if it even ever becomes reality. The truth of the matter is China is burning coal - imports up 51% from Australia in one year - like there is no tomorrow, seriously increasing the likelihood there will not be. The U.S. coal industry is in a mad rush to build some 150 new plants before mandatory carbon caps, carbon taxes or carbon sequestration are put in place. Coal ignited the industrial revolution - accounting for about 60% of human released carbon dioxide to date. The logical consequence of continuing to burn the 3500 gigatonnes of carbon found in the world's remaining coal reserves will prove deadly. If the world's remaining coal is burned, the planet would be several times past the concentration of carbon dioxide considered able to be adapted to safely. Each of the hundreds of new plants being built by China and the U.S. are without the latest commercially untested carbon sequestration technologies and will spew carbon dioxide directly into the atmosphere for at least 50 years. In the world of nine billion consumers to come, with the condition of the atmosphere in such tatters, the majority of the world's filthy coal reserves must be left in the ground as we transition exclusively to clean renewable energy alternatives. Thankfully, wherever new coal plants are planned protests are emerging including ending the bank's coal financing. King Coal, R.I.P., or the Earth and civilisation die. www.climateark.org

Arctic Death Knell Foretells Abrupt Climate Change

Arctic ice is disintegrating at an amazing rate, an indicator of how quickly global heating is occurring, and with grave consequences for the Arctic's absorption of heat, and the survival of polar bears and humanity. One of Canada's six ancient Arctic ice shelves has cracked off northern Ellesmere Island, creating an enormous 66-square-kilometre ice island and leaving a trail of icy blocks in its wake. Occurring 16 months ago, the enormity of the event is just now becoming known. The relatively rare Canadian ice shelves, located about 800 kilometres south of the North Pole, are 90 percent smaller than they were when first crossed in 1906. Meanwhile, astonishingly the melting of Arctic sea ice and precarious decline of polar bears has finally caught the attention of the Bush administration. The Department of the Interior has decided the iconic polar bear should be listed as "threatened" under the Endangered Species Act (ESA) because "the polar bears' habitat may literally be melting." Scientists predict that the Arctic Oceans summer sea ice could melt entirely as early as 2040 and possibly sooner. Open seas absorb more heat than sea ice which largely reflects incoming solar radiation. As a society we are so far behind on developing and implementing policy to address climate change that it is sadly, shockingly frightening.

Global Warming - **FACTS**
The Ozone Layer

T he ozone layer is the part of the Earth's atmosphere which contains relatively high concentrations of ozone (O3). "Relatively high" means a few parts per million - much higher than the concentrations in the lower atmosphere but still small compared to the main components of the atmosphere. The ozone layer was discovered in 1913 by the French physicists Charles Fabry and Henri Buisson. Its properties were explored in detail by the British meteorologist G. M. B. Dobson, who developed a simple spectrophotometer that could be used to measure stratospheric ozone from the ground. Between 1928 and 1958 Dobson established a worldwide network of ozone monitoring stations which continues to operate today. The "Dobson unit", a convenient measure of the total amount of ozone in a column overhead, is named in his honour.

The photochemical mechanisms that give rise to the ozone layer were worked out by the British physicist Sidney Chapman in 1930. Ozone in the Earth's stratosphere is created by ultraviolet light striking oxygen molecules (O2), splitting them into individual oxygen atoms (atomic oxygen); the atomic oxygen then combines with unbroken O2 to create ozone, O3. The ozone molecule is also unstable (although, in the stratosphere, long-lived) and when ultraviolet light hits ozone it splits into a molecule of O2 and an atom of atomic oxygen, a continuing process called the ozone-oxygen cycle, thus creating an ozone layer in the stratosphere, the region from about 10 to 50 km (32,000 to 164,000 feet) above Earth's surface. About 90% of the ozone in our atmosphere is contained in the stratosphere. Ozone concentrations are greatest between about 15 and 40 km, where they range from about 2 to 8 parts per million. If all of the ozone were compressed to the pressure of the air at sea level, it would be only a few millimetres thick.

Ozone-oxygen cycle in the ozone layer.

Ten percent of the ozone in the atmosphere is contained in the troposphere, the lowest part of our atmosphere where all of our weather takes place. Tropospheric ozone has two sources: about 10 % is transported down from the stratosphere while the remainder is created in smaller amounts through different mechanisms.

Although the concentration of ozone in the ozone layer is very small, it is vitally important to life because it absorbs biologically harmful ultraviolet (UV) radiation emitted from the Sun. UV radiation is divided into three categories, based on its wavelength; these are referred to as UV-A, UV-B, and UV-C. UV-C, which would be very harmful to humans, is entirely screened out by ozone at around 35 km altitude.

UV-B radiation can be harmful to the skin and is the main cause of sunburn; excessive exposure can also cause genetic damage, resulting in problems such as skin cancer. The ozone layer is very effective at screening out UV-B; for radiation with a wavelength of 290 nm, the intensity at Earth's surface is 350 million times weaker than at the top of the atmosphere. Nevertheless, some UV-B reaches the surface. Most UV-A reaches the surface; this radiation is significantly less harmful, although it can potentially cause genetic damage.

Depletion of the ozone layer allows more of the UV radiation, and particularly the more harmful wavelengths, to reach the surface, causing increased genetic damage to living organisms.

The ozone layer can be depleted by free radical catalysts, including nitric oxide (NO), hydroxyl (OH), atomic chlorine (Cl) and bromine (Br). While there are natural sources for all of these species, the concentrations of chlorine and bromine have increased markedly in recent years due to the release of large quantities of man-made organohalogen compounds, especially chlorofluorocarbons (CFCs) and bromofluorocarbons. These highly stable compounds are capable of surviving the rise to the stratosphere, where Cl and Br radicals are liberated by the action of ultraviolet light. Each radical is then free to initiate and catalyse a chain reaction capable of breaking down over 10,000 ozone molecules. Ozone levels, over the northern hemisphere, have been dropping by 4% per decade. Over approximately 5% of the Earth's surface, around the north and south poles, much larger (but seasonal) declines have been seen; these are the ozone holes.

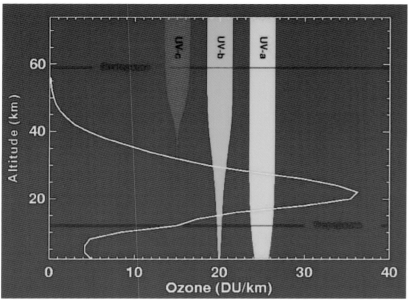

Levels of ozone at various altitudes and blocking of ultraviolet radiation.

On January 23, 1978, Sweden became the first nation to ban CFC-containing aerosol sprays that are thought to damage the ozone layer. A few other countries, including the United States, Canada, and Norway, followed suit later that year, but the European Community rejected an analogous proposal. Even in the U.S., chlorofluorocarbons continued to be used in other applications, such as refrigeration and industrial cleaning, until after the discovery of the Antarctic ozone hole in 1985. After negotiation of an international treaty (the Montreal Protocol), CFC production was sharply limited beginning in 1987 and phased out completely by 1996.

On August 2, 2003, scientists announced that the depletion of the ozone layer may be slowing down due to the international ban on chlorofluorocarbons, chemical compounds containing chlorine, fluorine and carbon. Three satellites and three ground stations confirmed that the upper atmosphere ozone depletion rate has slowed down significantly during the past decade. The study was organised by the American Geophysical Union. Some breakdown can be expected to continue due to CFCs used by nations which have not banned them, and due to gases which are already in the stratosphere. CFCs have very long atmospheric lifetimes, ranging from 50 to over 100 years, so the final recovery of the ozone layer is expected to require several lifetimes.

Compounds containing C-H bonds are being designed to replace the function of CFC's (such as HFC), since these compounds are more reactive and less likely to survive long enough in the atmosphere to reach the stratosphere where they could affect the ozone layer.

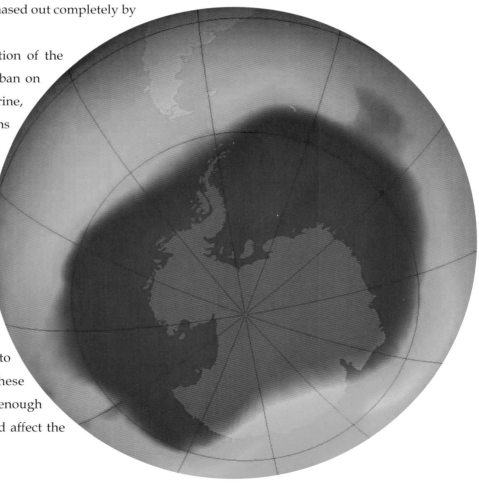

Kyoto Protocol United States

T he United States, although a signatory to the protocol, has neither ratified nor withdrawn from the protocol. The signature alone is symbolic, as the protocol is non-binding over the United States unless ratified. The United States is as of 2005 the largest single emitter of carbon dioxide from the burning of fossil fuels.

On July 25, 1997, before the Kyoto Protocol was finalised (although it had been fully negotiated, and a penultimate draft was finished), the U.S. Senate unanimously passed by a 95–0 vote the Byrd-Hagel Resolution which stated the sense of the Senate was that the United States should not be a signatory to any protocol that did not include binding targets and timetables for developing as well as industrialised nations or "would result in serious harm to the economy of the United States". On November 12, 1998, Vice President Al Gore symbolically signed the protocol. Both Gore and Senator Joseph Lieberman indicated that the protocol would not be acted upon in the Senate until there was participation by the developing nations. The Clinton Administration never submitted the protocol to the Senate for ratification.

The Clinton Administration released an economic analysis in July 1998, prepared by the Council of Economic Advisors, which concluded that with emissions trading among the Annex B/Annex I countries, and participation of key developing countries in the "Clean Development Mechanism" — which grants the latter business-as-usual emissions rates through 2012 — the costs of implementing the Kyoto Protocol could be reduced as much as 60% from many estimates. Other economic analyses, however, prepared by the Congressional Budget Office and the Department of Energy Energy Information Administration (EIA), and others, demonstrated a potentially large decline in GDP from implementing the Protocol.

The current President, George W. Bush, has indicated that he does not intend to submit the treaty for ratification, not because he does not support the Kyoto principles, but because of the exemption granted to China (the world's second largest emitter of carbon dioxide. Bush also opposes the treaty because of the strain he believes the treaty would put on the economy; he emphasises the uncertainties which he asserts are present in the climate change issue. Furthermore, the U.S. is concerned with broader exemptions of the treaty. For example, the U.S. does not support the split between Annex I countries and others. Bush said of the treaty: "*This is a challenge that requires a 100% effort; ours, and the rest of the world's. The world's second-largest emitter of greenhouse gases is the People's Republic of China. Yet, China was entirely exempted from the requirements of the Kyoto Protocol. India and Germany are among the top emitters. Yet, India was also exempt from Kyoto ... America's unwillingness to embrace a flawed treaty should not be read by our friends and allies as any abdication of responsibility. To the contrary, my administration is committed to a leadership role on the issue of climate change ... Our approach must be consistent with the long-term goal of stabilising greenhouse gas concentrations in the atmosphere.*"

Despite its refusal to submit the protocol to Congress for ratification, the Bush Administration has taken some actions towards mitigation of climate change. In June 2002, the American Environmental Protection Agency (EPA) released the "Climate Action Report 2002". Some observers have interpreted this report as being supportive of the protocol, although the report itself does not explicitly endorse the protocol. At the G-8 meeting in June 2005 administration officials expressed a desire for "practical commitments industrialised countries can meet without damaging their economies". According to those same officials, the United States is on track to fulfil its pledge to reduce its carbon intensity 18% by 2012. The United States has signed the Asia Pacific Partnership on Clean Development and Climate, a pact that allows those countries to set their goals for reducing greenhouse gas emissions individually, but with no enforcement mechanism. Supporters of the pact see it as complementing the Kyoto Protocol while being more flexible, but critics have said the pact will be ineffective without any enforcement measures.

In September 2006 the journal Nature reported that the National Oceanic and Atmospheric Administration had blocked an internal report which concluded that global warming caused by greenhouse gas emissions may be contributing to the frequency and strength of hurricanes.

The Administration's position is not uniformly accepted in the U.S. For example, Paul Krugman notes that the target 18% reduction in carbon intensity is still actually an increase in overall emissions. The White House has also come under criticism for downplaying reports that link human activity and greenhouse gas emissions to climate change and that a White House official and former oil

industry advocate, Philip Cooney, watered down descriptions of climate research that had already been approved by government scientists, charges the White House denies. Critics point to the administration's close ties to the oil and gas industries. In June 2005, State Department papers showed the administration thanking Exxon executives for the company's "active involvement" in helping to determine climate change policy, including the U.S. stance on Kyoto. Input from the business lobby group Global Climate Coalition was also a factor.

Furthermore, supporters of Kyoto have undertaken some actions outside the auspices of the Bush Administration. In 2002, Congressional researchers who examined the legal status of the Protocol advised that signature of the UNFCCC imposes an obligation to refrain from undermining the Protocol's object and purpose, and that while the President probably cannot implement the Protocol alone, Congress can create compatible laws on its own initiative. Nine north-eastern states and over 180 mayors from US towns and cities, have pledged to adopt Kyoto-style legal limits on greenhouse gas emissions. On August 31 2006, the California Legislature reached an agreement with Governor Arnold Schwarzenegger to reduce the state's greenhouse-gas emissions, which rank at 12th-largest in the world, by 25 percent by the year 2020. This resulted in the Global Warming Solutions Act which effectively puts California

At home, shopping or in the garden - you can make a difference.
Take action for our living planet by following these tips.

In your home

Turn off equipment like televisions and stereos when you're not using them. That little red standby light means they're still using power - and that means a contribution to global warming.

Save water:
- turn off the tap when brushing your teeth.
- collect the water used to wash vegetables and salad to water your houseplants.

Call your local government to see if they have a disposal location for used car batteries and other hazardous household wastes.

Recycle your paper, glass, plastics and other waste. Call your local government to find out if they offer a collection service.

Use rechargeable batteries.

Send e-greetings instead of paper cards. Check out the range of free WWF e-cards available.

Help reduce the world's rubbish dumps - don't use "throw-away" products like paper plates and napkins, and plastic knives, forks, and cups.

Out shopping

Take your own bags to the shops to carry home your groceries and shopping.

Look for products that have less packaging.

Buy organically grown fruits, vegetables, cotton clothing, and hemp-fibre products.

Don't buy bottled water if you know your tap water is safe - transporting water from its source to the supermarket shelves is an expensive waste of energy. And the plastic and glass bottles add to the already-high mountains of rubbish that we produce. Find out from your municipality about your tap water. If you do buy bottled water, buy from a local source (read the labels) and buy water that comes in recyclable glass or plastic.

Choose biodegradable cleaning products so that the chemicals have fewer negative impacts on the soil and water system.

Buy the most energy-efficient household appliances you can afford.

Use recycled paper.

Simply Google *Environment Websites* and start helping the world right now...

In the garden

Collect rainwater to water your flowers.

Let part of your garden grow freely and see what wild flowers appear.

Plant local species of trees.

Never take plants or pick flowers from anywhere in the wild.

Buy bulbs from cultivated stocks only (ask the shop or gardening centre for advice).

Stop using chemical pesticides - try to use natural products instead.

Try to attract birds to your garden as they eat aphids and other gardeners' pests.

Use traps, parasites, and natural predators such as ladybirds.

Use plants that repel insects. Some herbs and flowers - including basil, chives, mint, marigolds, and chrysanthemums - mixed in with other plants, help keep pests away.

Use disease-resistant and pest-resistant plants.

Use Neem oil and mix it up with some garlic oil (which you can make it home) to spray on tree trunks and diseased plants and shrubs. This works like a charm on pests, bacteria and fungus.

Remove the weeds by spraying them with something to adjust the pH (acidity) in the ground around them. Perhaps use some vinegar directly on the most stubborn ones.

Use organic compost and mulch to improve soil health and reduce the need for pesticides and fertilisers.

Don't use peat in your flower beds and vegetable gardens (peat is taken from ancient bog land, destroying some of our most precious wildlife areas). Instead, make your own compost with grass clippings and vegetable scraps from the house. Find out how to make your own compost.

Choose drought tolerant plants like Nepeta Six Hills Giant (Catmint). It looks like huge lavender flowers but uses very little water.

Pick only drought or Xeriscape friendly grass seeds that don't require as much as water to maintain.

Don't use electrical equipment like leaf-blowers as they consume so much energy for so little gain. Use a rake instead - it's better for your health too!

Take time out to sit out in your backyard with friends and family, and appreciate the beauty of nature!
http://www.panda.org

Switzerland

View from the Baeregg station at the east flank of Mount Eiger where hundreds of tons of rock are expected to fall, above Grindelwald, Switzerland, Saturday, July 15, 2006. The spectacular mass of rock breaking off the Eiger mountain has become an unexpected tourist attraction for the resort of Grindelwald. Hundreds of hikers and journalists have taken up position each day to watch the Eiger slowly shed a large chunk of its eastern flank, and ponder what it says about global warming.

Jerusalem

Palm trees and the golden dome of the Rock Mosque in Jerusalem stand covered with snow Friday, January 28, 2000. A rare snowstorm dumped at least 15 inches of snow on Jerusalem and covered the northern Negev Desert, toppling trees, closing roads and isolating cities throughout Israel.

Malaysia

American Erik Fearn strapped on the oxygen tank of his scuba gear while doing his morning outdoor workouts in Kuala Lumpur, Malaysia, Thursday, Aug. 11, 2005. Fearn, a travel writer and photographer, has become an incongruous sight in the suburb of Bukit Kiara as he zips past joggers dressed in a white sun visor, black scuba shorts and a yellow oxygen tank on his back.

SUNRISE
Kuala

Millions of Malaysians in Klang Valley, which includes the main city Kuala Lumpur, capital Putrajaya and biggest harbour Port Klang, reel from the noxious, smoke-filled haze.

Venice

Cafe tables and chairs are submerged in water in a flooded St. Mark Square in Venice, Italy, Saturday, Dec. 3, 2005 following high tide. Extreme weather conditions in this region which is the most vulnerable to rising seas are already cause for concern as Venice slowly disappears into the ocean.

Italy

A wave of cold, snow and ice which hit the Italian peninsula was sufficiently harsh to freeze even the salty lagoon waterways of Venice.

Seville

Seville, southern Spain, Thursday Nov. 23, 2006. This 14 meter, 46 ft. catamaran will be the first solar powered boat to attempt to cross the Atlantic Ocean. Boat builders are exploring new methods of using natural energy.

Kyoto Protocol China

China insists that the gas emissions level of any given country is a multiplication of its per capita emission and its population. China endorses this because of the advantage it would get within the new restrictions. Because China has emplaced population control measures while maintaining low emissions per capita, it claims it should therefore in both the above aspects be considered a contributor to the world environment. China considers the criticism of its energy policy unjust. China is currently the second largest emitter of greenhouse gases, and is expected to become the largest by 2030.

EVIDENCE

China

Chinese girls play on parched land in Nanning, southern China's Guangxi province, Saturday, Nov. 11, 2006. A severe drought in southern China left more than 2.4 million people short of drinking water.

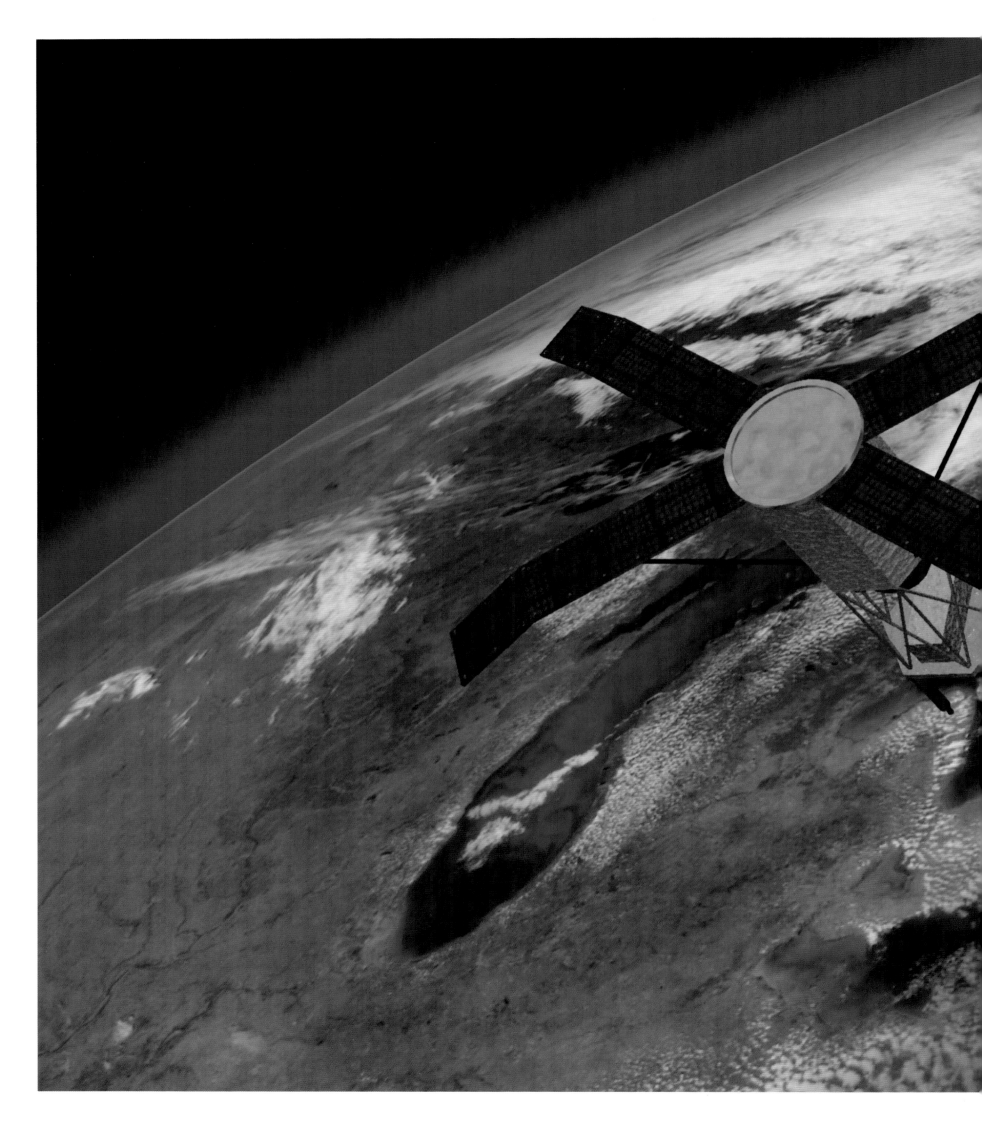

Climate

The NASA SeaWiFS (the Sea-viewing Wide Field-of-view Sensor) is designed to pioneer new global environmental observations and research. By providing a regular picture of the planet's colour, SeaWiFS helps researchers learn about the state of the world's interconnected ecosystems. The critical base of the ocean food web is shrinking as the world's seas warm.

China

Water almost submerges a bridge in Dazhou, in China's southwestern Sichuan Province Friday, July 8, 2005. At least nine people were killed and six were missing after the heaviest rains in a century hit the city, cutting roads and submerging buildings.

Cuba

A Cuban police officer fights unusually cold weather as he patrols a street in Old Havana, Cuba, where temperatures hit -8 C (17 F), Friday Jan. 24, 2003. Cuba is experiencing extreme weather patterns as a direct result of global warming.

Milan

Flowers are covered with snow during an early snowfall in Milan, Italy. An unexpected early winter storm brought several centimetres of snow across parts of Europe.

Switzerland

Cows graze on a snow-covered pasture of the Flueelapass, at a height of 2,200 meters, near the town of Davos, Switzerland, Friday, Aug. 4, 2006. Heavy rain hit parts of Switzerland, with snow falling at heights above 2,000 meters.

Genoa

A man looks out to sea as the 'gozzi' local fishing boats are covered in snow in the small harbour of Boccadessa, near Genoa, northwestern Italy, Thursday, March 3, 2005. A cold spell from Siberia hit the Italian peninsula characterised by unusually chilly temperatures for March in all cities.

Belgrade

A lightning strikes a cross on St. Mark's church during a thunderstorm in Belgrade, Serbia, Saturday, July 29, 2006. An unexpected thunderstorm and showers hit the country's capital in the evening, bringing some refreshment in the midst of a heat wave.

Lahore

Central Lahore city after heavy rain, Friday, July 1, 2005 in Pakistan. According to police sources, six people were killed as some parts of Pakistan received heavy monsoon rains following a long and severe heat wave.

Belgrade

A cargo ship is stranded by the low water level of the Sava river in downtown Belgrade, Serbia. Serbia is experiencing heatwaves with temperatures reaching 33 degrees Celsius (91 degrees fahrenheit), with the River Danube reaching its lowest level in the last 160 years.

New Zealand

Icebergs drift off the coast of New Zealand on Nov 3, 2006. The icebergs - two large ones and several smaller chunks - have sparked overseas interest as people clamour to view a once-in-a-lifetime occurrence that are now only a 30 minute flight from the southern city of Dunedin.

Srinagar

A child looks out from an auto rickshaw driving through a flooded street, as rain falls in Srinagar, India, Thursday, July 13, 2006. Heavy rainfall has been recorded in almost all parts of Kashmir bringing respite to the people from the intense heat wave .

Andermatt

Workers cover parts of the Gurschen glacier at the Gemsstock (2961 metres above sea level) above the Swiss ski resort of Andermatt with plastic sheets in an attempt to protect the glacier from melting. An area of around 2500 square meters was covered with the plastic.

Philippines

Villagers are dwarfed by giant windmills built by the Danish Development Agency, DANIDA, along the shores of Bangui, Ilocos Norte province in northern Philippines Wednesday Nov. 8, 2006. The sixteen giant "Bangui Windmills" are capable of generating 54 Megawatts of electricity and are the first such alternative source of energy in Southeast Asia.

STUDY
Earth

NASA's Ice, Cloud and land Elevation Satellite (ICESat) provided this 3-D graphic view of the Earth. The scientific data and photos are helping scientists understand how life on Earth is affected by changing climate. After less than a year of work, the Earth-orbiting satellite has churned out the most detailed, three-dimensional maps ever of the ice sheets blanketing Greenland and Antarctica. The baseline measurements collected by the Ice, Cloud and Land Elevation Satellite, or Icesat, should allow scientists to track the growth and shrinkage of the ice sheets, and to gauge the effect that might have on global sea levels.

Czech

An aerial view of flooded houses near the South-Bohemian city of Veseli nad Luznici on Friday, March 31, 2006. Due to rain and unusually warm weather which melted deep snow, rivers across the Czech Republic caused nation-wide floods.

Indonesia

A mosque is seen still standing in this aerial view of the town of Meulaboh in Aceh province, Indonesia, which was flattened by tidal waves on Saturday, Jan. 1, 2005. More Tsunami's are expected to hit the region in the future.

Australia

A Sydney Catchment Authority employee stands on a sandbank at Warragamba Dam showing the water level in the lake west of Sydney, at 16 meters (52 feet) below where it should be. Sydney's largest reservoir that provides water to Australia's largest city of 4 million residents, officially slipped below 40 per cent Thursday, Nov 2, 2006 as the effects of Australia's drought continue to diminish major cities water supplies.

New Orleans

A tattered American flag flies in front of the blown out Hyatt Hotel in New Orleans after Hurricane Katrina devastated the area on Monday, Aug. 29, 2005.

China

Tourists gather on the bank of the Qiantang River to watch tidal waves in Hangzhou, in east China's Zhejiang province Wednesday September 21, 2005. The tidal waves are an annual event and reach their highest around the Moon Festival, or the 15th of the eighth month of the lunar calendar.

Romania

Birds perch on a snowy bench in a Bucharest, Romania, park, Saturday, Feb. 25 2006. Cold weather and snowfalls affected most of Romania following days of unusual warm weather this week causing wildlife to take shelter from the sudden snowstorms.

Czech

A man walks across the flooded river Dyje in the city of Vranov nad Dyji, the Czech Republic, Thursday, March 30, 2006. Rivers across the Czech Republic were rising fast due to rain and unusually warm weather which melted snow that fell over the winter. Authorities have been anxious to prevent a repetition of the August 2002 flooding, which devastated a large part of the country and killed at least 16 people.

China

A local walks past a building which collapsed when torrential rains from Tropical storm Kaemi made landfall in Pinghe, southeastern China's Fujian province, Wednesday July 26, 2006. Heavy rain from Tropical Storm Kaemi collapsed a levee in southern China, threatening to flood the homes of 20,000 villagers as soldiers filled the breach with sandbags and tree stumps.

California

A setting sun begins to fade from a deep red colour as it burns through the haze over the palm tree-lined Chateau Fresno Avenue near Fresno, California. The San Joaquin Valley, a virtual trough for ozone pollution stretching through central California, is classified as a ``severe'' violator of clean air standards, according to standards established by the U.S. Department of Environmental Protection.

Canada

A polar bear plays on the tundra near Churchill, Manitoba, Canada, in this recent photo. Animal and plant species have begun dying off or changing sooner than predicted because of global warming. Cold-adapted species, such as emperor penguins have dropped from 300 breeding pairs to just nine in the western Antarctic Peninsula. Polar bears are dropping in numbers and weight in the Arctic.

Chinese women wear plastic bags to protect their hair and face during a severe dust storm in northern China. Nearly every spring, dust storms blow off the dry expanses of the Mongolian desert plain.

Paris

Parisians try to cool off near the foot of the Tour Eiffel, as temperatures soared to 36C (96.8F), in Paris, Tuesday, July 25, 2006. The scorching temperatures have revived memories of the deadly summer of 2003, when 15,000 people in France died from the heat, many of them were elderly people left alone while families vacationed.

Beijing

Chinese commuters' bikes are parked awaiting the return of their owners at at the entrance of a metro station in Beijing, China Monday July 31, 2006. China needs to quickly build better urban transport networks and find ways to reduce vehicle emissions or it will face increasingly serious environmental and energy problems. Chinese cities need to urgently build up their bus and subway networks "before the critical mass of motorists is formed and shapes an irreversible, auto-dependent land use pattern."

China

One of the serious negative consequences of mainland China's rapid industrial development has been increased pollution and degradation of natural resources. A 1998 World Health Organisation report on air quality in 272 cities worldwide concluded that seven of the world's 10 most polluted cities were in China.

China

Bicycle riders try to ride to safety in heavy rain Thursday May 18, 2006 in Shanghai, China. Typhoon Chanchu pummelled southern China where it flooded scores of homes in an area where officials evacuated more than half a million people. Chanchu was the most severe typhoon to strike the South China Sea region during the month of May and was blamed for 37 deaths in the Philippines.

Ahuge flock of crows scared locals in Boldog, some 60 kms from Budapest on Saturday, Dec. 16, 2006. Thousands of crows invaded the fields near the village pilfering the open crops in unusually warm weather.

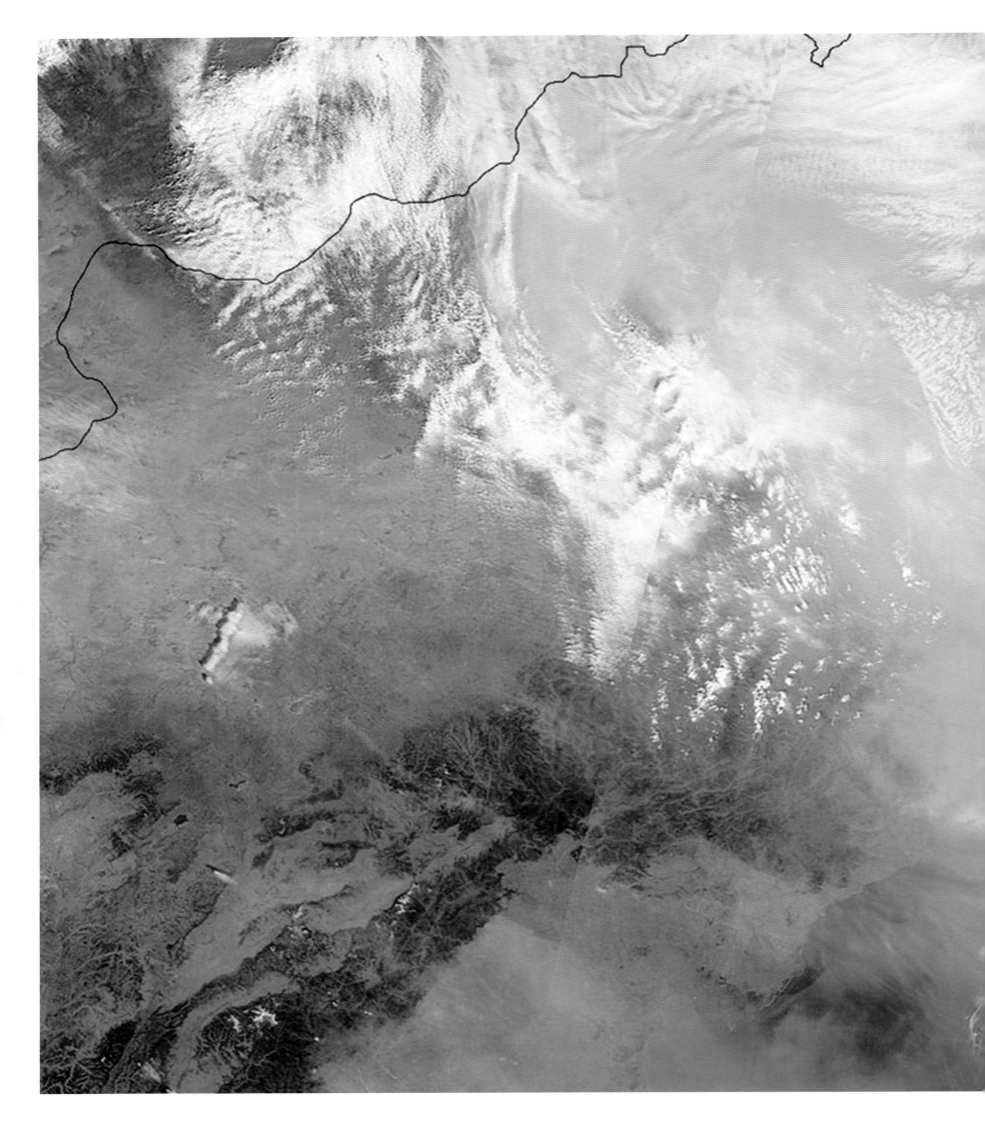

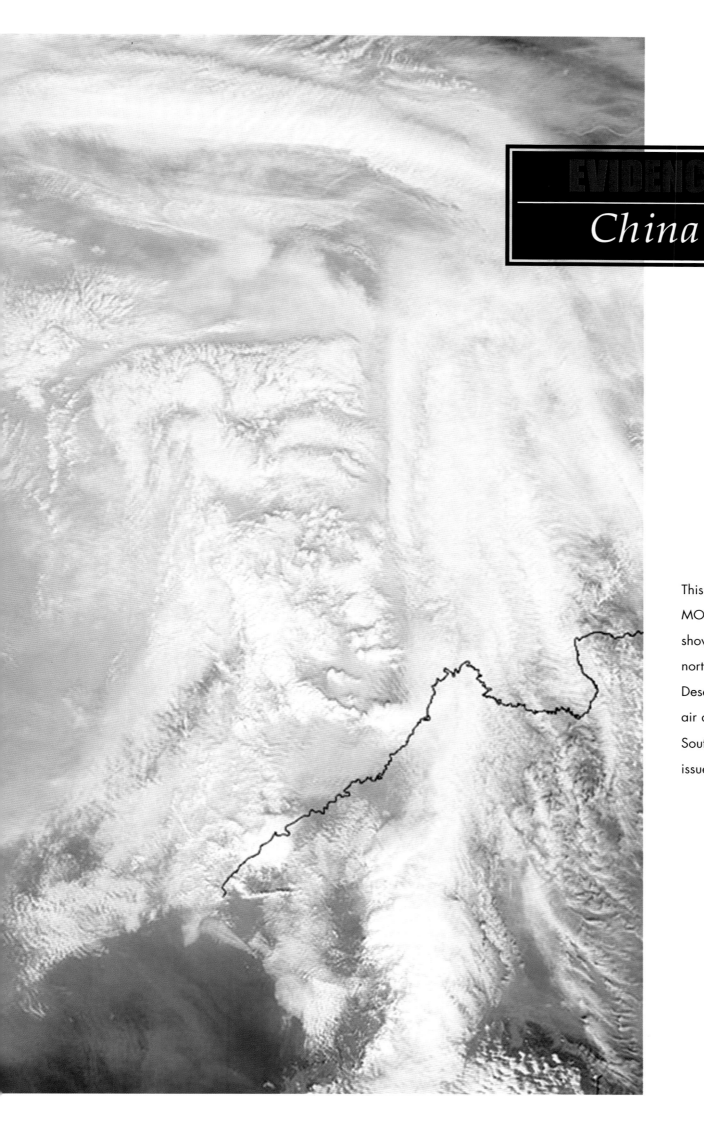

This latest image provided by NASA MODIS Land Rapid Response Team shows dust and pollution over northeastern China on April 7, 2006. Desert dust from China also polluted air and raised health concerns in South Korea, where authorities issued a Yellow Dust warning.

Marshall Islands

Ankit Stephan at the edge of a lagoon in Majuro, Marshall Islands, whose encroaching waves are toppling shoreline coconut trees. Ocean waters are rising because of global warming are eating away at beaches across the Pacific.

United States

A farmer cuts a field in Ticonderoga N.Y. as steam rises from the International Paper mill nearby on Monday, Nov. 6, 2006 . The mill began a two week test burning of reclaimed tires as an alternate source of fuel. The New York State Dept. of Environmental Conservation and the U.S. Environmental Protection Agency issued permits for the test despite protests from Vermont over worries of an increase in air pollution.

India

People walk on dry desert as their village is seen fully submerged under floodwaters at Malva village, in Rajasthan state's Barmer district, India, Monday, Aug. 28, 2006. Torrential downpours and floods killed at least 132 people and left scores missing in the desert region of Barmer in western India. The normally drought-prone district was under a sea of water after the unusually heavy rains which weather experts described as a "freak phenomenon" caused by global warming.

Morocco

This satellite image shows an unusual dust storm over Morocco with strong winds sweeping thick Saharan Desert dust off the coast of Morocco out over the Canary Islands in the Atlantic Ocean. The true-colour image was acquired by the Moderate Resolution Imaging Spectroradiometer (MODIS) aboard NASAs Aqua satellite.

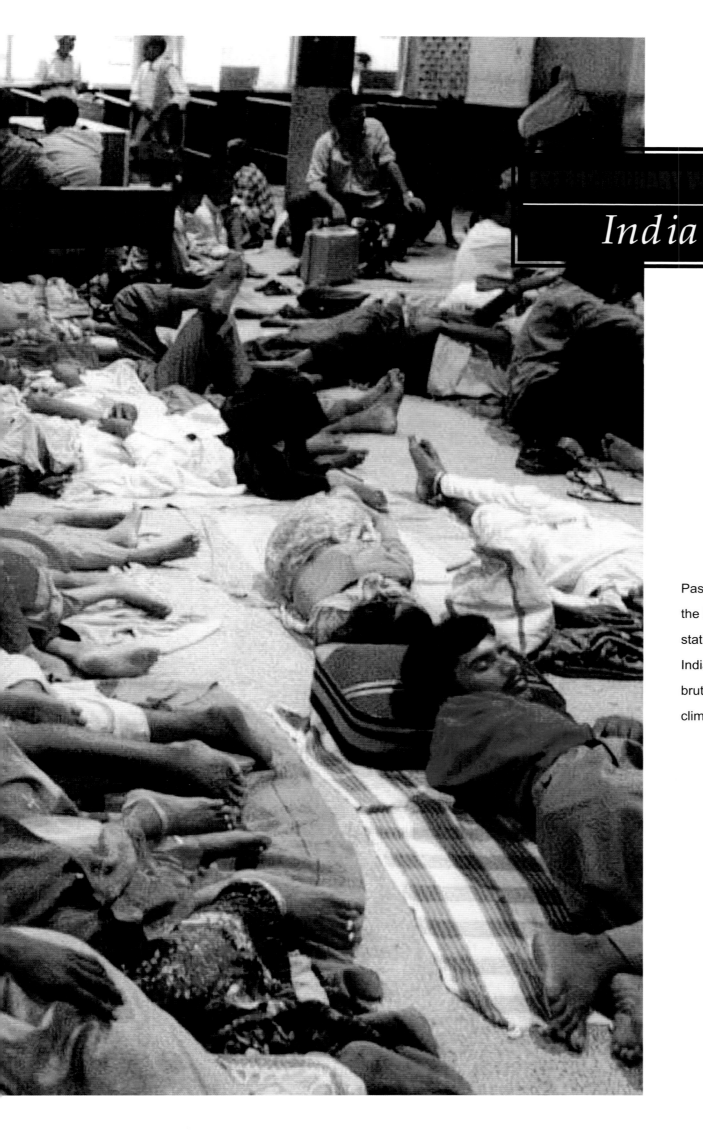

EXTRAORDINARY WEATHER

India

Passengers waiting for trains rest in the heat of Secunderabad railway station near Hyderabad, southern India. The toll of people killed by a brutal heatwave in southern India climbed to 622.

Kansas

Kylea Lewis sits in a refrigerator to stay cool while taking a break from life-guarding at the Oakland Community Pool in Topeka, Kansas, Tuesday, July 18, 2006. Weather officials extended a heat advisory in the eastern half of the state, where the humidity was making it feel like 115 degrees.

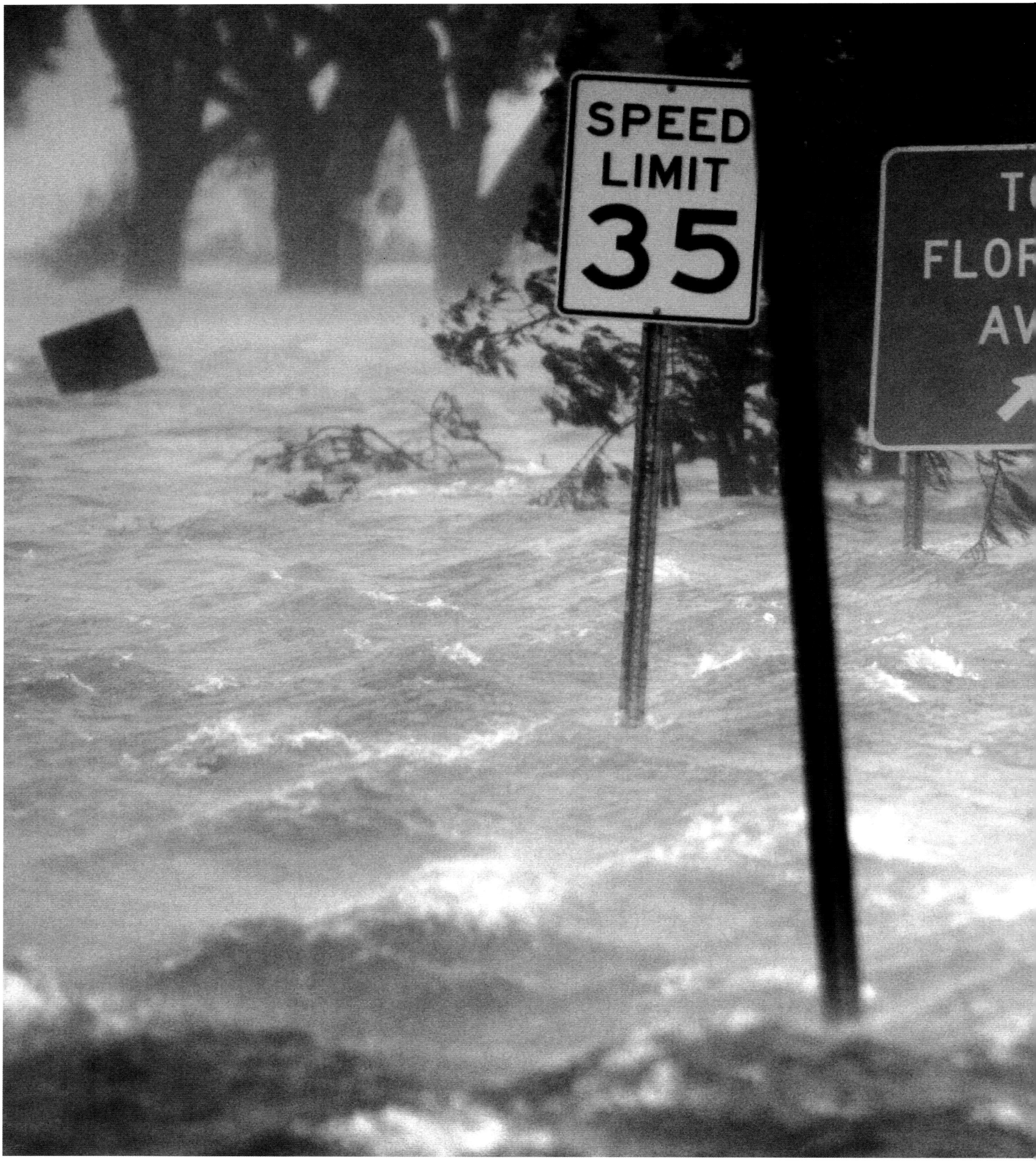
SPEED
LIMIT
35

United States

The global risk of hurricane disaster is increasing due to human activity. Populations are concentrating along the world's coastlines—particularly in large urban areas. Improved forecasting and emergency response have lowered hurricane casualty rates, but as more people and infrastructure move into harm's way, storms are likely to become more destructive.

Heavy clouds hang over Hangzhou, capital city of east China's Zhejiang Province, as Typhoon Haitang churned into southeastern China Tuesday, July 19, 2005, bringing torrential rain and high winds to coastal areas where more than 1 million people had fled their homes.

These pictures of Kuala Lumpur show clear sky, left, taken in Jan., 2005 and haze sky, taken on Aug. 10, 2005. Air pollution exceeded emergency levels in two Malaysian towns as a smoky haze from forest fires in Indonesia shrouded Kuala Lumpur and its suburbs in a pall of noxious fumes in the country's worst environmental crisis since 1997.

Anchorage

A skier poses for a photograph on Portage Lake in front of Portage Glacier, March 29, 2006 about 50 miles south of Anchorage, Alaska. The Portage Glacier, which is a major Alaska tourist destination near Anchorage has retreated so far it no longer can be seen from a multimillion-dollar visitors centre built in 1986. Anchorage Mayor Mark Begich is hosting conference for leaders from 17 states to get a firsthand look at the effects of global warming on the northern landscape.

In common with many other forms of transport, aircraft engines emit polluting gases, contribute to global warming and global dimming, and cause noise pollution. Modern turbofan and turboprop engines are considerably more fuel-efficient and less polluting than earlier models. However, despite this, the rapid growth of air travel due in large part to low cost carriers is contributing to an increase in total pollution attributable to aviation. In the context of global warming and peak oil, there is an ongoing debate about possible taxation of air travel and the inclusion of aviation in an emissions trading scheme, with a view to ensuring that the external costs of aviation are taken into account.

Johannesburg

Homeless people warm themselves around a fire on a sidewalk in downtown Johannesburg, South Africa Monday, May 22, 2006. The Salvation Army distributed soup and blankets to the homeless as an unexpected cold front hit the region with temperatures plummeting to below freezing.

United States

These photos released by the Glacier National Park Archives show the dramatic recession of the Grinnell Glacier as seen from from the summit of Mt. Gould in Glacier National Park, Mont. in 1938, from left, 1981, 1998, and 2005. Upper Grinnell Lake continues to enlarge as the glacier recedes. Icebergs can be seen floating in Upper Grinnell Lake in the recent photos.

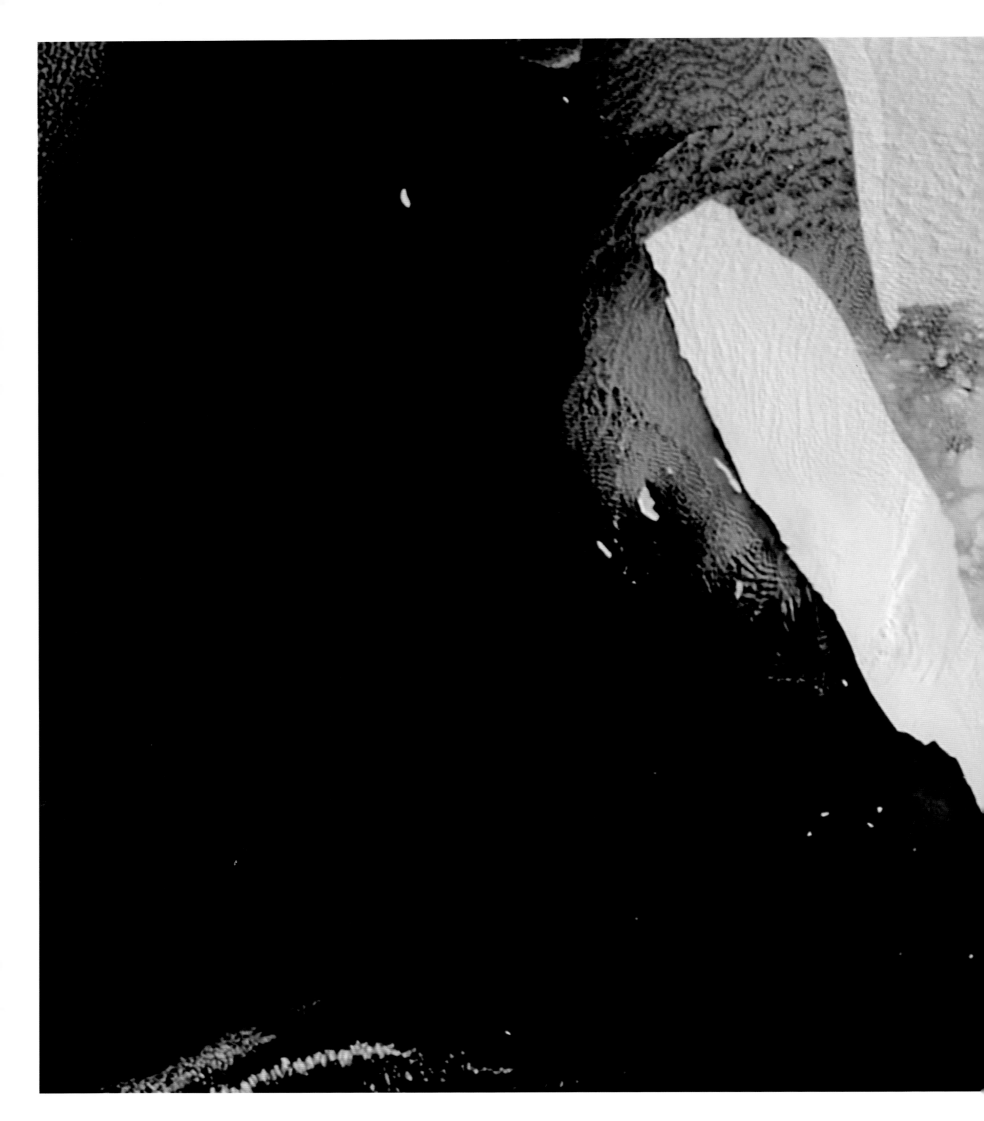

Antarctica

In this Jan. 17, 2005 satellite image released by NASA, a 160-kilometre (100-mile) long iceberg, known as B15A, seen in the centre, stops short of a collision with a 100-kilometre (60-mile) long ice block known as the Drygalski Ice Tongue in the southern ocean near the U.S. McMurdo Research Station in Antarctica. Scientists believe the floating berg must have run aground just five kilometres (3.1 miles) short of smashing into the giant Ice Tongue. Iceberg B15A, with an area of 3,120 square kilometres (1,200 square miles) has been dubbed "the largest floating thing on the planet." U.S. researchers estimate it contains enough water to feed Egypt's Nile River complex for 80 years.

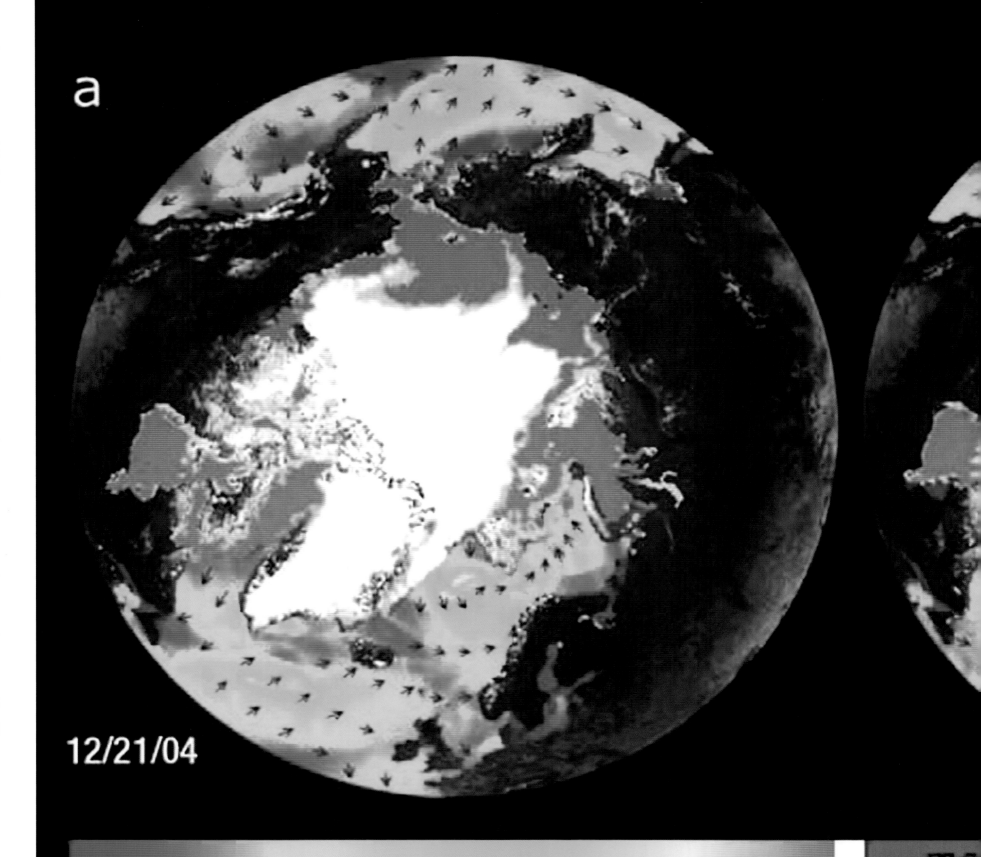

a

12/21/04

0   Wind speed (m·s⁻¹)   40

b

STUDY

Arctic Sea

12/21/05

seasonal mixed perennial

Sea ice classes

This image provided by NASA on Wednesday Sept. 13, 2006 shows QuikScat interannual observations of sea ice over the Arctic enabling the detection of recent drastic reductions in the extent of perennial ice and its depletion from the eastern Arctic Ocean between 2004, left and 2005. Arctic sea ice in winter is melting far faster than before. For more than 25 years Arctic sea ice has slowly diminished in winter by about 1.5 percent per decade. But in the past two years the melting has occurred at rates 10 to 15 times faster.

An aerial view shows a landslide from heavy rains of typhoon Aere in Wu Feng village Thursday, Aug. 26, 2004 in Hsinchu county, northern Taiwan. The mudslide wiped out 24 homes Wednesday, killing 15 although many residents had been evacuated before the typhoon began battering the island. Aere is the strongest storm to threaten Taipei and killed at least 30 people in Taiwan, Japan and China.

United States

An aerial view of a flooded neighbourhood on the east side of New Orleans, Thursday, Sept. 1, 2005 after Hurricane Katrina passed through the area leaving a devastated city.

A New Orleans resident walks through floodwaters coated with a fine layer of oil in the flooded downtown area on Tuesday, Aug. 30, 2005. Hurricane Katrina was one of the strongest Hurricanes ever recorded and with the rise of global temperatures, it is expected that similar, stronger events will occur in the near future.

Pensacola Beach, Florida., is seen in this series of images with markers prepared and released by the U.S. Geological Survey in July 2005 showing rapid erosion along the shoreline. Overwash during both Hurricane Ivan and Hurricane Dennis extends inward covering the coastal road. Some of the houses present after Ivan but missing in Dennis were likely condemned and demolished sometime between the storms.

Chicago

A pedestrian steps through a morning downpour as she heads to work Thursday, July 20, 2006, in Chicago. Cooler temperatures followed the storm, a relief from several days of temperatures that peaked in the 90's. City officials said the heat contributed to a number of deaths in the recent heat wave.

Hybrid

The Hybrid/Electric vehicles now being introduced into the market reduce air pollution emissions due to lower fuel consumption, leading to improved human health with regard to respiratory and other illness. Composite driving tests indicate total air pollution of carbon monoxide and reactive hydrocarbons are 80 to 90 percent cleaner for hybrid versus conventional vehicles. Hybrids' greater fuel economy has implication for reduced petroleum consumption and vehicle air pollution emissions worldwide

China

A Chinese woman sleeps in the shade under an umbrella, using a squashed tomato to cool her forehead as temperatures peak during the afternoon sun in Beijing, China, Wednesday, June 22, 2005. Heatwaves hit northern China with temperatures reaching 42 degrees Celsius (108 F) in some places.

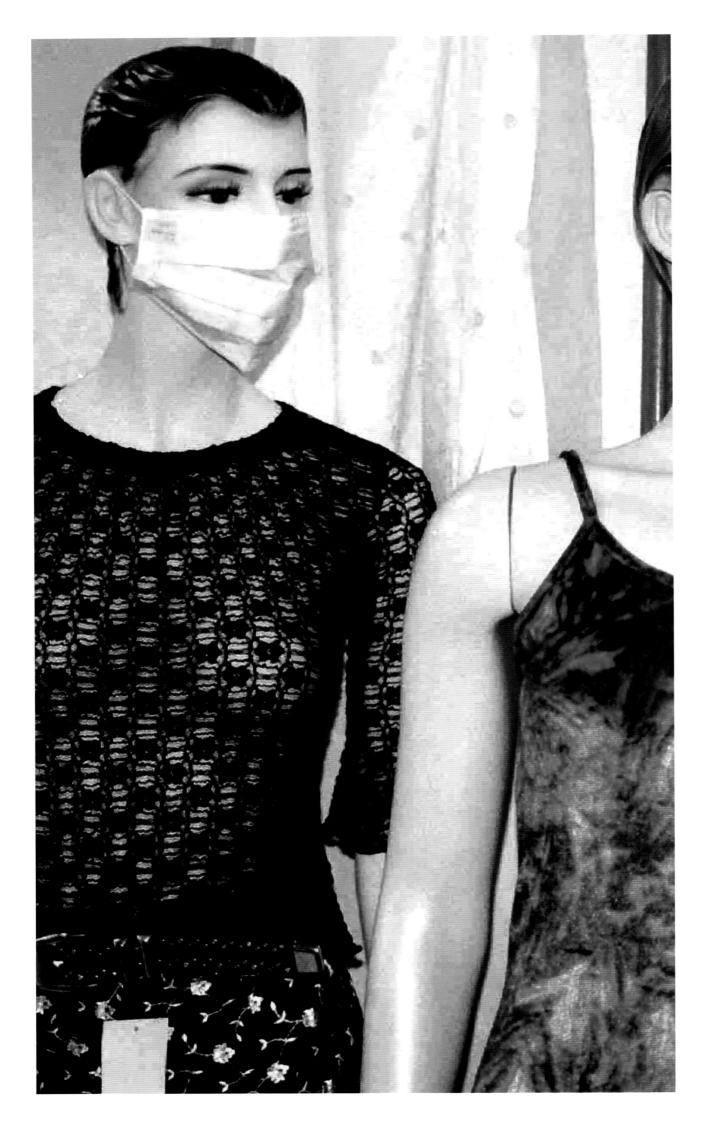

A boutique in Kuala Lumpur that produces coloured surgical masks as a fashion accessory to match their outfits display one on their mannequins.

Local Iraqis fight for ice slabs at a local icehouse, Thursday, July 28. 2005, in Baghdad, Iraq. With temperatures as high as 50 Celsius (122 Fahrenheit) and sporadic electricity in the home to run fans and air conditioners, ice has jumped from Iraqi Dinar $1,000 (US$0.70) to Iraqi Dinar $8,000 (USD$5.40) making it impossible for most to cool their homes.

Construction worker Eric Yanega pours water over his face as he takes a break from pouring concrete at a Monadnock high-rise building project in Brooklyn, New York, Tuesday Aug. 1, 2006. Health experts advise plenty of water to prevent dehydration as local temperatures rose to triple digits.

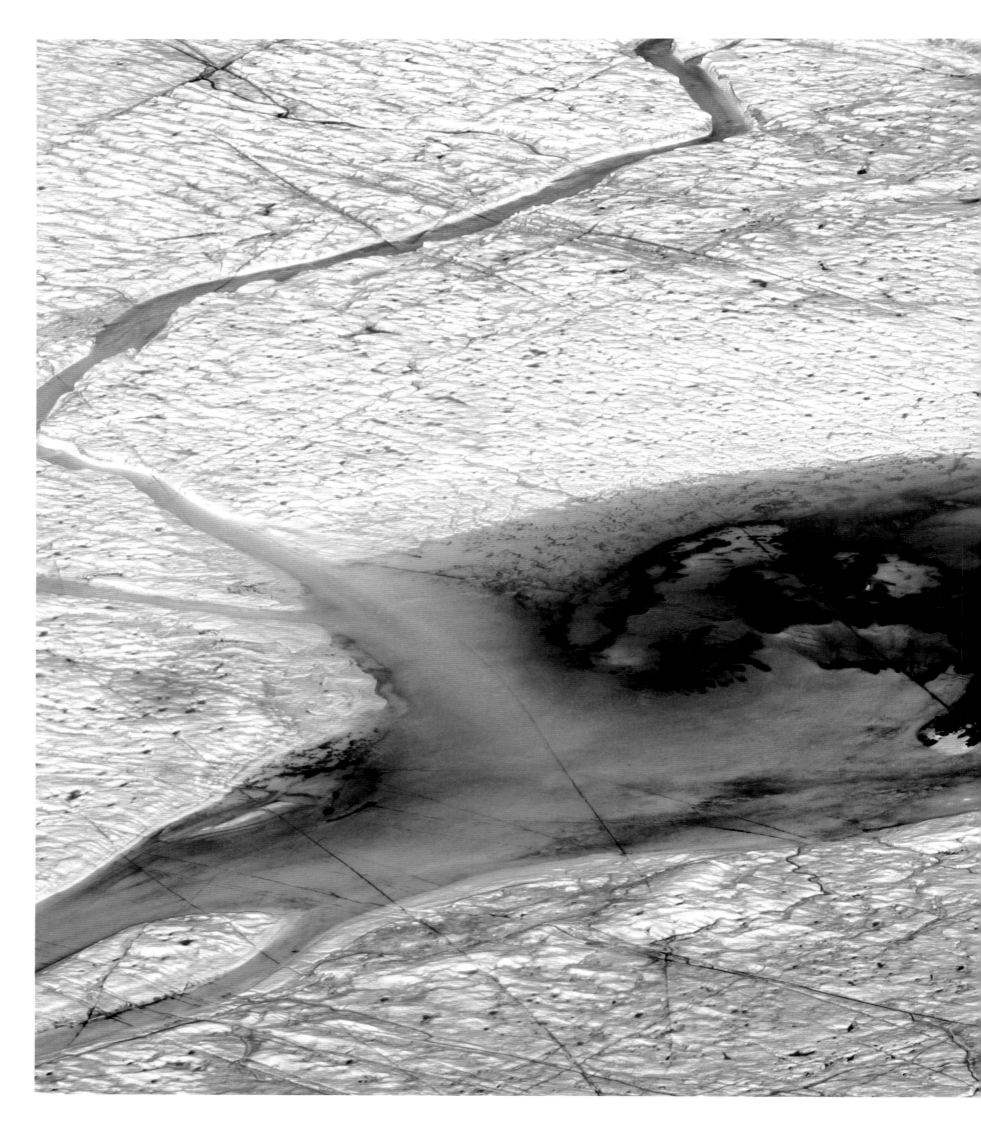

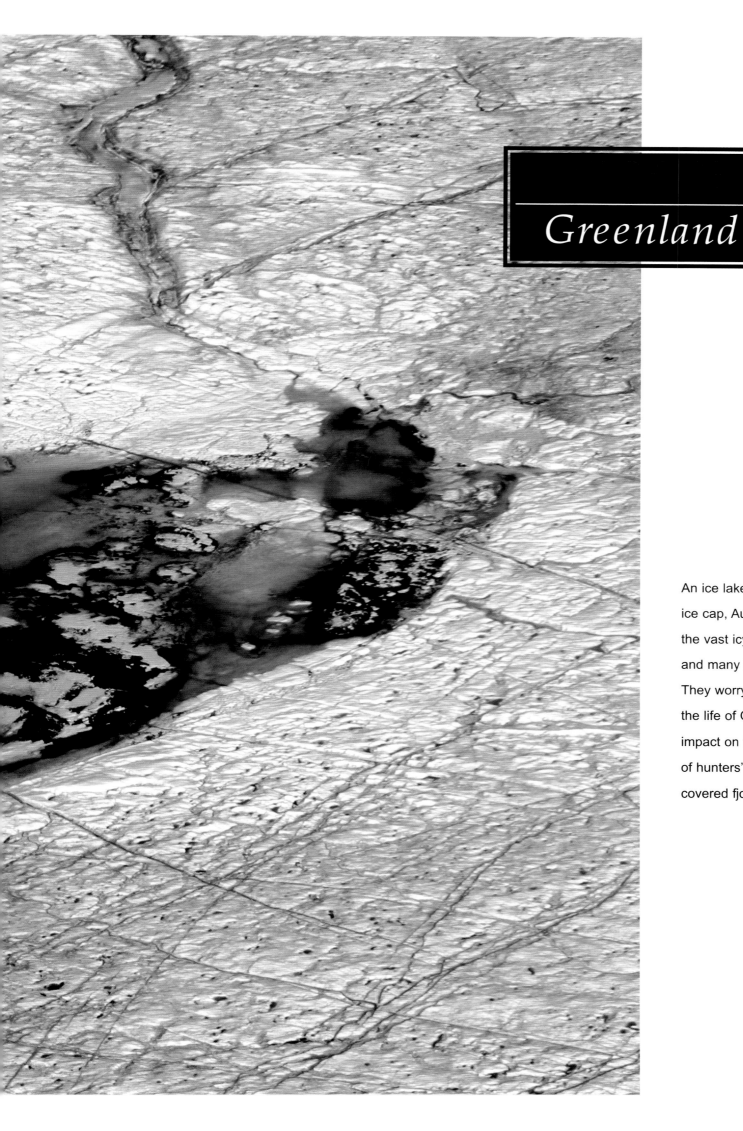

Greenland

An ice lake is seen in the Greenland ice cap, Aug. 17, 2005. Scientists say the vast icy landscape is thinning, and many blame global warming. They worry about the implications for the life of Greenlanders, from the impact on fishing stocks to the ability of hunters' dogsleds to cross ice-covered fjords and inlets.

Greenland

About 85 percent of Greenland is covered by ice, which is up to 3,200 meters (10,560 feet) thick and is moving. Patterns show the ice is being pressed away from the middle of the island, glaciers sliding slowly between mountains before breaking off into icebergs that float out of the fjords. NASA satellite monitoring shows Greenland glaciers dumping water into the sea at twice the rate of 1996. Such melting land ice is helping raise sea levels, along with the expansion of seawater as it warms.

Kuala

Tourists are left to view what could be the capital city of Kuala Lumpur cloaked with a thick haze at Kuala Lumpur Tower , Wednesday, Aug. 10, 2005. Air in many parts of Malaysia turned unhealthy as a weeklong haze blamed on forest fires in neighbouring Indonesia worsened.

Brazil

This view of Iguazu falls shows it unusually dry, less than one-fifth its normal size, in Brazil on Saturday, July 29, 2006. The name of the falls comes from the Guarani Indian word meaning "great water." In 1986 Iguacu Falls were declared a Natural Heritage of Mankind by UNESCO. Although the dry spell in southern Brazil's winter has reduced the volume of the Iguacu River, it has not endangered energy production at the nearby Itaipu hydroelectric dam, Brazil's largest.

Maasai women took to the streets of Nairobi Kenya Saturday, Nov. 11 2006 to protest that industrialised nations are doing too little to curb global warming.

Australia

Goulburn town council water utilities manager Matthew O'Rourke does his weekly checks at Pejar Dam, the main water supply for the town and region in 180 kilometres (99.4 miles) from Sydney Friday, May 13, 2005. The dam is at less than 10% capacity causing drastic water restrictions. O'Rourke said the region close to the national capital, Canberra, needs twice its annual rainfall for four years running to replenish the water supply.

Spain

A man walks with a dog along a dry cracked reservoir bed in Alcora, eastern Spain. The world - especially the Western United States, the Mediterranean region and Brazil - will likely suffer more extended droughts, heavy rainfalls and longer heat waves over the next century because of global warming.

Tourists snorkel around Upolu Cay on the Great Barrier Reef near Cairns off the Australian north east coast. Greenpeace Australia released a report which said that if the current rate of climate change continues, the world s coral reefs may be wiped out within 100 years. Global warming is causing a damaging condition known as coral bleaching which is striking the world's reefs more often and with greater intensity than ever before.

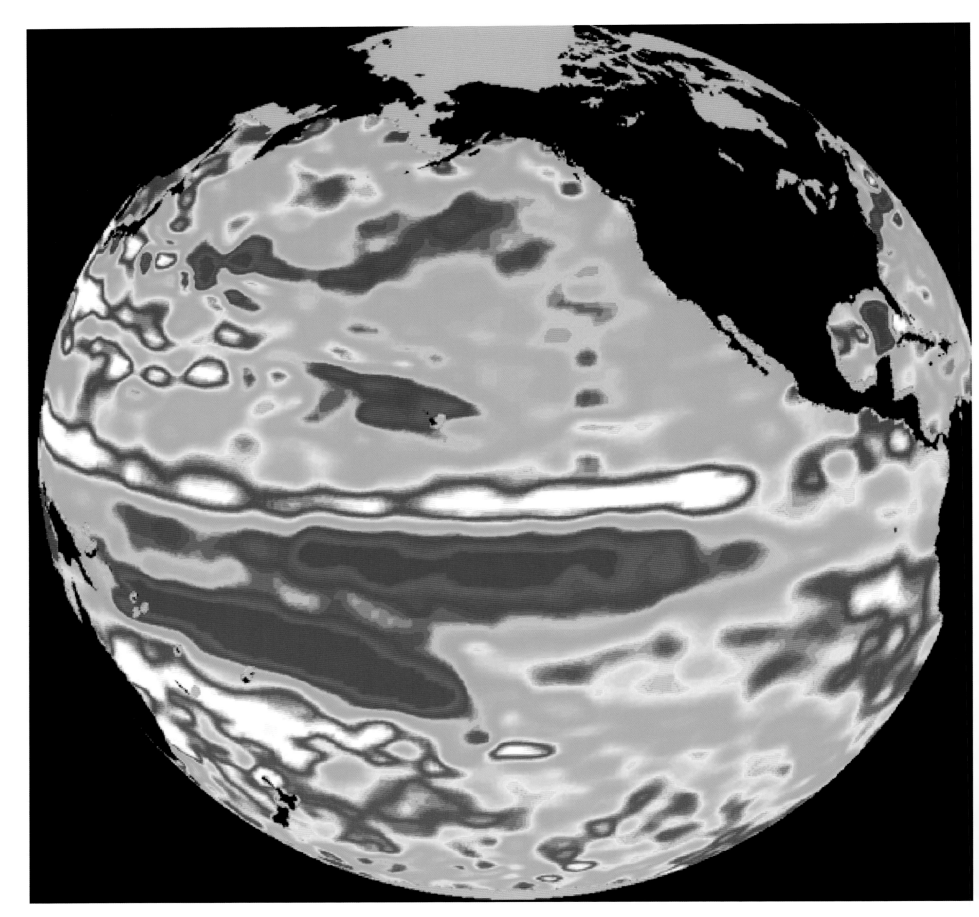

A recent image of the Pacific Ocean from the TOPEX/Poseidon satellite, taken from NASA's Jet Propulsion Laboratory's web site. The image shows that colder waters, represented by the purple shaded areas, are spreading into the tropical Pacific region dominated in the last year by El Nino.

Dusseldorf

The bank of the Rhine on Friday, 25. July 2003. The long lasting drynesses and the heat saw the water level fall far under normal conditions. Because of the low water line, larger ships could transport only 30 to 50 per cent of their freight.

Koblenz

A row of houses along the Rhine River in Niederwerth, near Koblenz, are partly submerged after the river broke its banks and flooded parts of the town, Saturday, March 24, 2001.

ENVIRONMENTAL DISASTER
New Orleans

Hurricane Katrina left behind a landscape of oil spills, leaking gas lines, damaged sewage plants and tainted water. More than 500 Louisiana sewage plants were damaged or destroyed, including 25 major ones. There were about 170 sources of leaking hydrocarbons and natural gas.

Hamburg

View of the flooded landmark Fischmarkt (fish market) in downtown Hamburg, northern Germany, early Friday, Jan. 12, 2007, after a heavy storm hit Germany.

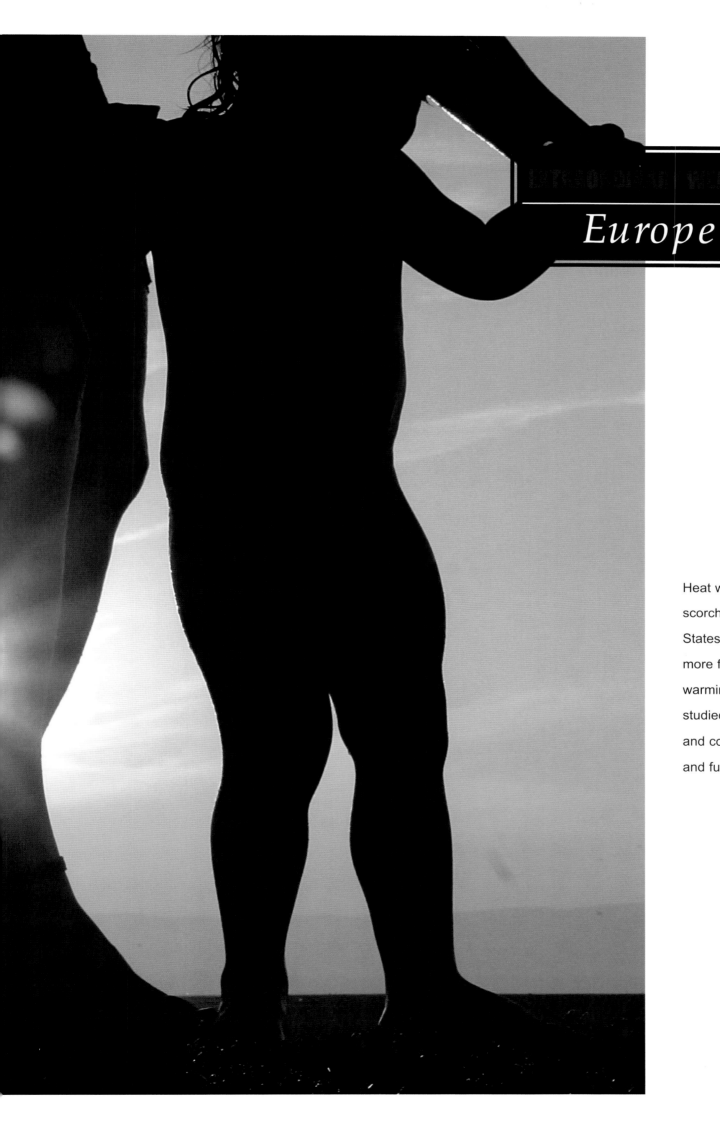

Europe

Heat waves like those that have scorched Europe and the United States in recent years are becoming more frequent because of global warming, say scientists who have studied decades of weather records and computer models of past, present and future climate.

United States

Looking at a database of 1,166 forest wildfires from 1970 to 2003 in the western United States, researchers compared the number and potency of wildfires to spring and summer temperatures and the timing of snowmelts. Wildfire season and potency increased "suddenly and dramatically" in the late 1980's, the scientists say.

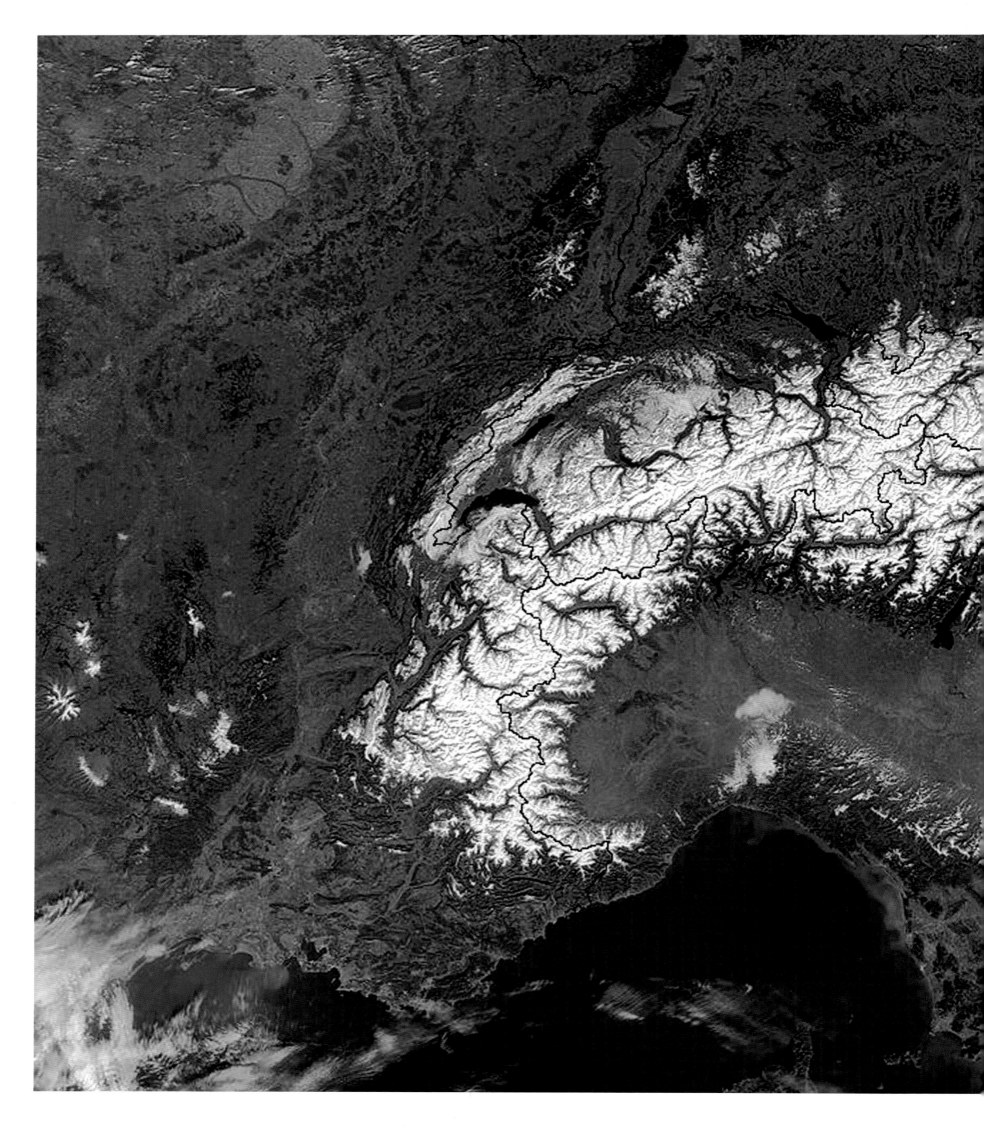

European

Europe's Alpine region is going through its warmest period in 1,300 years. The European study notes that similar warming occurred in the 10th and 12th centuries, though those periods were not quite as warm as current readings.

Higher sea temperatures are disrupting delicate coral biosystems, causing a devastating phenomenon known as "Coral Bleaching." Coral thrives and gets its beautiful coloration from a symbiotic relationship with algae. When the water gets too warm and bright, the algae leaves the coral, which then loses its color and becomes susceptible to disease.

Comparison photos of Muir and Riggs Glaciers in Glacier Bay National Park and Preserve, Alaska. Muir glacier, parts of which were greater than 65 meters thick in 1941, has retreated out of the image in 2004 (towards the upper left). The distance to the visible Riggs glacier in 2004 is 3 km. During this time, the Muir Glacier retreated more than 20 km.